man and his environment: law

EARL FINBAR MURPHY

The Ohio State University

Harper & Row, Publishers
New York
Evanston
London

**man
and his
environment:
law**

*Library of Congress Catalog
Card Number:
77-132661*

**to my
two
nephews,
kevin
and
scott
kocher**

contents

editors' introduction

The books of the Harper & Row series being published under the general title of *Man and His Environment* are designed to help us understand the world about us, our dependence on it, and what we are doing to it, both good and bad.

From the personal point of view, it has been said that the environment is everything else but me. It is the sky over our heads and the earth beneath our feet. It is other people and any living animal or plant with which we have any connections. It includes what the senses of sight, hearing, taste, smell, and touch tell us about nature. Also, the environment is home, the cities and towns we have built. It includes the landscape that is altered by raising food, feed, and fiber; by the extraction of minerals; by building homes, schools, churches, places of business, and factories, and by building facilities for travel and transport, for the generation of energy, and for communication. The environment includes not only the natural and manmade things about us but also physical and cultural conditions and processes.

All these elements of the environment can be studied, thought about, and worked with individually, but this analytic approach is inadequate for the understanding of the total environment, and it leads to difficulties when we overlook or neglect the consequences of single-purpose actions. This is because the elements of the environment do not occur singly in nature or in culture, but in complex interacting systems. For example, soil is not just decomposed rock. It includes air and water, hundreds of organic and inorganic compounds, and almost innumerable living things, most of which are too small to be seen in a handful of dirt. Water is a simple compound, but we are not likely to encounter it as such. Many substances are dissolved in it, particles are suspended in it, and living creatures float and swim about in it. Everywhere we find mixtures of things, in a drop of pond water, a lump of soil, a breath of air, most things that man makes. Not only do we find mixtures of things everywhere; these things interact with one another because of processes of their own, changing one another and the conditions of the whole.

In this book of the series Earl Finbar Murphy has dealt with one important facet of the interrelations between man and his environment. For each of these books, no matter what is the main focus (climate, energy, materials, waste, food, population, recreation, transportation, law, or aesthetics and the cultural roots of our viewpoints), we have asked the authors to take a holistic point of view and to write about interconnections, interactions, consequences, and, in fact, the systems of man and nature together. As broad-gauged thinkers and scientists, they are well equipped for this demanding goal.

Man has become the leading cause of environmental change. He is discovering that he is responsible for much that he does not like—air and water pollution, poisons in our food, deteriorated cities—and that in order to correct such disagreeable, unhealthy, and unpleasant conditions he must understand the ecology of his environmental interrelations.

Although this book can stand alone, it is also an integral part of the series on *Man and His Environment*.

John E. Bardach
Marston Bates
Stanley A. Cain

acknowledgments

The author wishes to acknowledge the following organizations for sources of information not otherwise available to him, or available only upon a very abstruse chain of inquiry: the American Institute of Urban and Regional Affairs (AIURA); the Technical Board of the Institute for Development of Riverine and Estuarine Studies (IDRES); the Center for Research in Water Resources at Austin, Texas; the Athens Center of Ekistics; the Environmental Studies Board of the National Academies of Science and Engineering; the California Simulation Study of the Institute of Ecology, University of California at Davis; the Advisory Council on Human Settlements of Washington, D.C.; the John XXIII Institute; and the Ohio Conservation Foundation.

Naturally, none of these groups or organizations is responsible for what I have done with the information as I understood it. In addition, I am grateful for what I have learned through contact with the Franklin Institute of Philadelphia, Pennsylvania; the United States Office of Water Resources Research; the Temple University Institute of Law and Health Sciences; and the Advisory Committees of the Ohio State Water Resources Center and The Ohio State University School of Natural Resources on the subject of environmental regulation. These organizations, too, are not responsible for what I have done with the knowledge gained through this contact.

1
the environment as problems

man's drive to change nature

The control of his environment has been the purpose of man since circumstances separated him from other animals and enabled him to acquire the status of a separate species. If the prehistorians are correct in their appraisal of the remains in the Olduvai Gorge in East Africa, humankind was attempting even at 1,750,000 B.C. to build rude shelter from the elements and was shaping tools to facilitate the supplying of his food. If correct, it means the attempt to control environment is nearly coterminous with human existence.

Man must control nature through the dual means of physical techniques and social structures. These two means closely interact; and it is not simple to determine where the one ceases and the other begins. Clearly, tools are physical means of controlling the environment through technology. Yet the choice and purpose of all tools will be determined by the organization of the society possessing them. Important among the mental constructions making up the mores of any society will be the legal. Law is the aspect of each culture concerned with publicly ordering all behavior toward persons and things so that the group may carry on its routine conduct

1

without a continuous restructuring of basic relationships. The attitude that law in any society will assume toward nature will be determined by the kind of value each particular culture assigns to its environment.

There has never been a constant view of nature shared at all times by all societies. Some have seen their environment as one of intense hostility through which movement was possible only at greatest peril and from which support had to be torn. In such a condition man is an isolated atom, brought to his crises by the relatively vast power in the fierce hostility of nature and by the puniness of his own individual struggle for survival. Given such an outlook, any control man might possess would appear to him temporary and on so small a scale that nature scarcely could reflect his presence.

This, indeed, is the view that first emerges in most ancient literature. It is not true of all cultures, though. In some situations, despite the retention of the belief that man is slight whereas nature is massive, cultures have viewed their environments as benign. Usually nomadic, these people have been willing to move through the world, taking what was present, confident more would be offered, unaware of the extent to which they left an impress behind them, and refusing to see themselves at war with the forces from which their livelihood derived.

However, this seems to have been the less common view. More prevalent was the opinion that an enemy in nature was hard to placate. The more man wished to change what first he came to, the more he saw either an enormous impersonal indifference crushing to his aspirations or else a malevolent opposition delighting in foiling his every hope.

For such a viewer the world could be divided into two very uneven and unequally valued parts. One small, highly prized parcel was the "garden," an Eden perhaps to be more dearly cherished because it was a garden created not by God but by constant human effort. It had been through the subduing of the wilderness that the garden had initially been created. Only through similar effort could it be maintained; and only work at least as great could extend the garden. Certainly, given such a premise, the extension of the garden against the wilderness is a noble enterprise neither to be shirked nor doubted.

The garden, ideally, is everything the wilderness is not: benign, open, responsive to human design, expectable in every way even to little planned surprises included for variety's sake. Swamps are drained, forests felled, grasses cropped, soil broken for cultivation, rivers bounded, wells dug, fields plowed, and a situation is created which ultimately allows the emergence of historic man—settled, literate, urbane, prosperous, and though still hostile to the wilderness, quite content to believe he had himself created in the garden something good compared with the wild spaces where predators roamed and human life was a poor and chancy existence.

The garden was judged as being without fault in itself; indeed, it often received a religious endorsement. Its beauty and bountifulness were either a divine reward for human effort or the way God had first made the world before some cataclysm in Heaven had forced a change. The common agreement was God's own indifference or even hostility to the wilderness. Though everything might be His creation, nothing wild was equal to what man had changed.

risks in changing nature

The result could not be other than this. At least initially, man's first powers of judgment must relate to what is immediately serviceable to human health, prosperity, and comfort. For example, until very recently, it was quite difficult to find anyone willing to praise the merits of swamps. True, hunters might praise them for game; or some people, harried by enemies, might take refuge there. But swamps have mostly been regarded as unproductive and as barriers to progress and human well-being.

So pervasive has this attitude been, that the swamps' modern apologists have preferred to talk about the need to maintain "wetlands." Too much encouragement has

been given for too long for the removal of swamps to defend them under that name. Yet whatever their name,
they are not unqualified blights. Especially as they grow
scarcer, the functions performed by swamps (or wetlands, if preferred) become more clearly revealed.

They are, of course, sanctuaries for a variety of wildlife, places in which breeding, feeding, and resting during migration occur for birds, animals, fish, and smaller
species. Some of this life exists only in the swamp; but
for much of it, the swamp is simply a necessary stage in
the life process. Whatever function those species themselves serve—pollination, predation, or food supply, in
relation to other life forms—the swamp is vital to the
maintenance of their being.

Yet it is too easy to dismiss the swamps' importance
when seeing them only as habitat for wildlife. Important
as they may be, swamps also serve as recharge mechanisms for lakes and rivers, as filters to keep water clear
and pure, and as barriers against invasions of salty
ocean. The margin between land and sea is frequently a
soft and shifting one; but for all its quaky, watery quality,
the marshy shoreline may be a more effective protector
than a narrow, brittle band that can be broken or crept
under by the constant pressure of salt water. The coast
is in greatest danger when the line between land and
water has been most sharply drawn, with the marshes
drained and fields sloping down to the beach.

There is a similar risk for lakes when the supporting
swamps have been removed and their soils put to the
plow. Not only is there no longer a marsh to act as a
catch for waste and eroded materials, but the marsh's
own content is added to the sediment washing into the
nearby lake. The marsh no longer exists as a place on
which exuberant life can flourish. Instead, all this richness is passed into the lake or river to explode into an
existence that has too narrow a space to contain it. In
fact, it is a confinement made still tighter by the lack of
recharge water, kept previously with relative security
from evaporation in the recesses of the swamp but now
pumped away so that it can no longer seep in to replenish the diminished and overburdened lake or river.

the fiscal values
in changing nature

There are many inducements, of course, for drying up the wetlands. The water once lying there can be pumped away to irrigate other land too dry in its natural state to produce any, or as many, crops. The earth left behind, the muck land, is rich soil, the product of lush growth and consequent decay. Also, with the disappearance of standing water, the swarms of insects, often disease carriers, depart. Fever zones are rarely places where settlers care to move, and one solution is drying up all spots congenial for the breeding of mosquitoes, flies, and gnats. Fever apart, their absence improves the amenities and human settlement rises sharply.

With the swamps gone, every fiscal good seems to follow. What had previously been land without production has become a tract capable of growing crops, permitting the building of towns and industries, and in a cash economy producing money for those using it. Beyond this, the drained tract can be taxed, either directly in terms of its new value, or indirectly through a levy on its production or on the incomes of those responsible for that production. An area that before had seemed only counterproductive to everything man wanted to do in its vicinity might be raised to perhaps the highest level of productivity and human value by the single act of drainage.

This has occurred time after time. It could not be otherwise in the presence of growing numbers and of a steadily widening and deepening demand by those numbers for an ever-better life. Although cultures have existed content to float along on whatever resource base they have had available to them, history has presented a dominant strain that represents a rejection of that kind of adaptability. An insistence on a growth in well-being could be satisfied only by a massive change in resource conditions. In the presence of such a situation, swamps could be tolerated only as long as means were lacking to make the desired change.

Sometimes change has meant a new situation nearly as permanent as the condition replaced. This has been especially true in northern and northwestern Europe and South China. A combination of soils, climate, and husbandry made possible a change to a humanly productive and yet stable situation in which soil and water loss stayed at a minimum. For example, the southern shores of the Baltic and North seas originally were marshlands, capable of supporting scant population. The few who lived there saw no reason to change, however, having produced a successful swamp culture.

But passive acceptance of the swamps was not what the chiefs of the Teutonic invaders wanted. Christianization had opened the whole world to them; and they needed wealth and people supporting their ambitions. With only swamps behind them, those rulers could scarcely move out into the great world to whose affairs they were drawn. They would not adapt as had the earlier inhabitants and it was essential to change the face of the land. Fortunately for this purpose, the Cistercian Order had rediscovered the Roman engineering skill of swamp drainage; and to these monks vast tracts were given. What was conveyed had only a potential; but very quickly the monks altered it into the prosperous farmland, interspersed with busy towns, which has existed since the eleventh century. It is not a beautiful countryside; but it remains a stable one in balance with its own internal forces.

the instability
inherent in nature

Nature, after all, knows nothing static. The static condition is an impossibility, for living organisms are constantly involved in the processes of reacting, reproducing, and dying. At best, a balance of contending forces will be as close as nature can come to the unchanging, a balance made possible by the tension of elements in conflict. It is a tension that extends beyond the living organisms and affects such relatively inanimate parts of nature as soil and water.

When the swamps of northern Europe were drained, a sandy loam was revealed that could maintain its consistency and fertility almost indefinitely under the altered conditions. Drainage had not meant erosion of soil, silting of rivers, drowning of the coast in runoff water, or irreversible desiccation of the interior. Instead, it had meant a new natural balance that has lasted a thousand years without apparent deterioration.

South China, which seems to have a similar ecological history, has produced the same sort of balance, which has lasted more than twice as long. Ever since the Chinese moved into the southern region and replaced the primitives who had been content to take the land as it had always been, it has been an area capable of enormous production of human foodstuffs. Following the acquisition and conversion of this region to farm production, China moved into the first rank of world states, a move comparable, though on a far grander scale, with the translation to prosperity of the north German, Scandinavian, and Baltic states.

Northern Europe and South China are, however, the happy examples of the consequence of marshland conversion. This is not to say they are alone; but it is to say that such changes are more likely to produce an instability carrying catastrophe within it. Swamp drainage is successful—if success is measured in terms of human productivity under stable conditions over an undefinable time period—when there is a certain combination of soil, terrain, rainfall, vegetation, and human demand. If the combination is different, the result ultimately cannot be the same.

This is not to say that short-term results may not produce rich profits or that a correcting of deficiencies could not prolong a changed situation. But the new conditions are usually not capable of stability and forebode a bleak future for the region. In situations like these there is a steady slide toward a break that means a return to the swamp, or a collapse into something else—and a return to the swamp is not the worst of the possibilities.

The re-creation of the swamp is not, of course, to be lightly dismissed. It generally occurs because (1) cultivation causes a choking of river channels with silt, (2) drainage waterlogs bordering areas so that water being pumped away backs up underground, or (3) malaria appears to wear away the population. Each of these sets up a situation harder to cope with than the conversion of the virginal swamp. Channels must now be dredged, and soil that has been allowed to wash away and to become a perilous nuisance must be replenished. Water must be piped far enough to prevent its infiltrating back. And disease must be eradicated with all the difficulties accompanying the removal of the causes; anything less would be merely palliative.

Clearly, none of the above is ever a simple task, and yet a breakdown in the condition of a converted swamp can lead to less remediable results. Swamps often exist in areas where rainfall alone does not account for them. Ground conditions and topography rather than a gross amount of precipitation cause the water to accumulate. Sometimes this is the result of glaciation and sometimes the integral formative process of deltas, peninsulas, and coastal plains.

the wider
consequences
of changing nature

Yet waterlogging, such as has oppressed the seacoasts of western Asia, is the smallest problem stemming from drainage of swamps and deforestation. A far severer consequence is desiccation. When northern Europe and South China were drained, factors in their climates and soil structures were capable of maintaining stable ground and moisture conditions. But a similar consequence has not come about where swamps have been drained in large areas of North America stretching from Mexico to Wisconsin. What has happened here, beginning in the sixteenth century when the Spaniards initiated vigorous drainage in the Mexican Highlands, has been a drying of the landscape visible to even the casual observer.

A sixteenth-century traveler repeating four hundred years later the trip from central Mexico north through the middle of the continent to Canada would everywhere be struck by the increased dryness of the country, except as relieved by irrigation supplied from underground sources.

The swamps, wet prairies, and sometimes even the lakes would be replaced with dry land. In places, he would find the land so dried out that it would have sunk from lack of support by the withdrawn water; and this would be most true where the drying effects of human drainage had been carried out for the longest time, as in Mexico. He might find the countryside more immediately pleasant, but he would also have to note a profound alteration extending over centuries and leading apparently to an arid conclusion.

Human actions might slow down or even halt this trend by importing huge quantities of desalinated ocean water or water diverted south from sub-Arctic rivers. But any survivor of the sixteenth-century milieu would realize that without such actions aridity would be inevitable because there would be no means anywhere within the natural processes to overcome what man had been doing for over four centuries. The traveler would recognize that success in one particular had created a grave threat in another.

Too often the wealth present in the land is regarded as a treasure store to be ruthlessly exhausted—when, indeed, it is not treated as an expendable nuisance. The swamp in its watery state is seen merely as a menace to be removed. Its muck land is a resource to be used up —or used with minimal concern until production falters. In either case, the swamp is not looked on as any part of an on-going dynamic, integrally connected with everything living or renewing around it. To treat such a resource in so isolating a manner is to reduce it to the level of a bundle of money that can only be spent and never replenished. A bankroll so exploited can last only if expenditures are cut back or their rate of withdrawal is slowed down. Something in nature that has been isolated from its environment, of which a drained swamp is only one example, can behave no differently.

Though it is a common enough literary device to refer to nature as a treasury, a store, a warehouse of wonders, it would be a mistake to take these as accurate expressions of reality. Such words are poor analogies to describe a dynamic nature that is never static, always moving, and, because of this constancy in activity, forever seeking to renew the previous condition. Whatever appears to be permanent is instead a fine balance of tensions, sometimes far more brittle and unstable than what seems most in flux. Lumbermen, for instance, have repeatedly shown how heavily forested regions, appearing to be best suited to forests, were actually on the fragile edge of something very different, so that the clearing of the trees swiftly produced a radically and irreversibly altered description.

The living, self-replenishing world is actually far richer than any comparison to a storehouse of treasure. Nature, unless broken into exploited fragments cut off from sustenance, constantly replaces itself, whereas it has been the fate historically for every human treasury to be exhausted. But the natural world, wherever it has not fallen under a human management modeled on the operation or the plundering of a treasury, has kept up its wealth and has as much to offer the human exploiters today as at any time in the past. The dynamic, moving, renewing qualities in nature retain their activity and mock any comparison to the richest human treasury. The very risks to stores of human wealth given New Testament prominence—corrupting moth and rust—are simply part of the processes whereby nature continues itself and provides the wherewithal of man's exploitative needs.

man as the determinant

Natural dynamics, of course, are not easily apparent to man. Everything so apparently firm is actually energy in motion; and, for this reason, there is no end to the change in the physical universe, however remote it may be from the rapid alterations in the life mechanisms. Yet, as far as humanity is concerned, such comparative time differences make an enormous difference. What takes geologic epochs to produce is for man, with his relative brief existence as a species, endlessness itself. Indeed, so short is man's individual span that a replacement procedure taking a century—the briefest instant to nature —is to a man something that has taken far too long. The consequence of this is that from a human viewpoint it is intelligent to divide the environment into *stock resources,* which took eons to develop, and *flow resources,* which replenish themselves in briefer time units more comprehensible to the individual mind. Stock resource has all the potential for exhaustion implied by the word; flow resource is a term promising constancy. But whereas neither implication is quite true, the distinction is a valid one for human economics, based as it is on the time terms used for human life. It is the flow resources that have the most immediate significance for the quality of human life.

The center of reference is, of course, man. How could it be otherwise because nature is neutral? Nothing is a resource until man finds it necessary or useful to his needs or desires. The growing complexity of these needs and desires has drawn the universe nearly to the furthest star into the definition of a resource.

The term "pest" is not known in natural terms and is not easy to define in even a human vocabulary. True, certain organisms use others for food supply, or find others barring them from food, or are troubled in their health. Yet only for man does the moral dimension contained within the word "pest" exist, and, beyond that, the idea of amenity. This dimension gives to pest eradication the zeal so lacking in even the most omnivorous, nonhuman predator. Not only is man at the center of judgment; he judges for reasons far outside the limited needs of food supply or even more extended economic purposes. The fervor with which programs are undertaken to stamp out pests has a force behind it which can scarcely be explained only by economic reasons. In the study of resources man is the definer of all things in the absence of a universal calculus with referents that both include and transcend all human purposes. Despite the current use of mathematics and logic, such a calculus has not yet developed; and if it should appear, it still would be the creation and the object of a human manipulation.

This ought not be startling. It was by separating himself from nature through the invention of tools, fire control, speech, and command techniques over other humans that man began his history. Through this alienation and through the creation of highly artificial constructs man has been able to objectify the world about him so that it can be broken down into manageable bits to which such abstractions as "resources," "nuisance," or "cost-benefit" can be applied. In this way, as the distance between man and nature has increased, the human ability to affect, manipulate, and control the world around mankind has increased. Man's existence was inconsequential to the processes of the universe until his unity with nature was split. After nature became man's environment, what humanity did in the world became of accelerating consequence.

It is a result, too, from which there can be no turning back to an organic unity of man and nature. This is not possible because man has no primitive form in which he does not cause a profound disturbance in everything natural that he touches. The seemingly slight impact left by many nonliterate peoples of the past and present has lain in their few numbers. When their activities are more closely analyzed, it can be seen that what they demand from their hunting, grazing, or cultivating activities often exceeds the demands more sophisticated cultures make on their environment. In modern instances of larger population their economies have rapidly revealed just how severe their traditional requirements have been. When the demands are fully evaluated, it is evident man never had an Arcadian past to which he might return by some stroke of luck. Even a breakup of today's highly technical urban-industrial civilization would not bring about any such improvement. Instead, the survivors would be thrust into a struggle that could only continue the insults man has forever been imposing upon nature.

man's possibility of moderating his impact

Man's contemporary behavior to his environment is not entirely one of heedless conversion of its living and renewable parts into dissipating cash. An airplane journey over the American Midwest sees enormous evidence of soil defense: contour plowing, the deep markings of terraces, the strips of windbreaks, the tangles of drainage gullies allowed to return to wild growth. Perhaps much of this plains country ought never to have been settled; certainly settlement did make havoc with the native grasses that best protected the region, and without doubt the ground and surface water is suffering abuse. Yet within the full knowledge of these faults there has been since 1930 a shift to behavior of some promise, sufficient at least to delay a moving over to desert conditions that seemed a rapidly approaching certainty at that date.

Similar benefits have occurred for other parts of his environment that are resources to man. Water quality in the United States has generally improved since 1940 despite worsening cases like Lake Erie and the Hudson River. In some ways air quality, too, is better. The Black Cities of the nineteenth century, with their choking palls of soot, are gone. A few American municipalities have reduced their indexes of air pollutants and a national reduction program is under way. It is not all a question of hopelessness; and a 1968 prediction of UNESCO that the century's end will find the world direly suffering from the effects of air pollution is not a certainty. There are so many fragments of good news, in truth, that a rosy glow could be depicted as emanating from man's relation with his environment.

It would be misleading and defeating, however. The rosiness in the glow is still more one of destruction than salvation; and the good news is still the exception. The environment is more likely to be caught in a process of being used up than stabilized.

Despite considerable reforestation, for example, more trees are cut for lumber each year in the United States than are annually producing comparable timber. The deficiency is made worse by the replanting being mostly in softwoods and the heavy cutting of hardwood, with little regard for replacement. Lumber prices have fluctuated sharply; and despite techniques through veneers and pressings to make a little wood go much further, there is now an uncomfortable feeling among builders that the price of wood is too variable for reliable use. The logic of this would seem to call for greatly increased refores-

tation, particularly among hardwoods. Instead, the industry has insisted greater cutting should be allowed in federal and state forests to solve the crisis. A variety of
arguments have been brought up to show how beneficial
this would be to the forests as well as the lumber and
building industries; but, considering how the present forestry situation has developed, the opponents of increased cutting might well wonder if any benefits are at
stake here aside from cash dividends for the next few
years. Maybe technique will offer the way out through
hardwood substitutes made of cellulose. But whatever
the outcome possible through invention, it would be the
simplest sort of optimist who would take only comfort in
present United States forest conditions or who would see
only solutions rather than problems in the general area
of man's unstabilizing effect on his environment.

man's traditional refusal of moderation

Since the eighteenth century humanity has increasingly
suffered from a kind of claustrophobia. This might be
due to an oppressive sense of human overcrowding, a
perception that has been given more and more common
expression in the past two centuries. But it is more likely
a shut-in feeling resulting from the comparison of human
desire and the milieu from which that desire must be satisfied. At first it was continents that were too confining,
then the globe, and later the aerial stretches about the
globe. Already the human mind reaches to the furthest
limits of the universe, even as it plans to follow up space
adventures in depth with life colonies for the moon and
other planets.

On the basis of past intellectual history, space experiments, too, will begin to lose the luster of frontiering;
and then the whole universe will begin to cramp and
close in upon the questing human mind, compelling a denial of the meaning of the word "universe" and forcing a
moving out into zones beyond. For good or ill, this seems
to be the future, unless the social and economic bases
for such explorations are disrupted. Yet barring an un-

precedented effectiveness to those disruptions probably requiring a near elimination of humanity, or at least of its technically advanced part, there would be only delay. From the beginning of the human condition the aggression has all been toward an ever-greater separation from and mastery of nature by man; and what was true of humanity in its formation is not likely to diminish at a later stage where the techniques exist to make effective that aggressive assertion of superior power over nature's mechanisms.

This assumed to be the case, the course best suited is not one of direct opposition or of repining. Indeed, the formation of an opposition is probably not a possibility. What has once seemed so has later often turned out to be the same exploitation disguised as conservation. It is only necessary to follow the history of high dams through the literature to see a program that began as Dr. Jekyll, to emerge several decades later as a Mr. Hyde. Other examples could be adduced; but there is no reason to do so, once it is realized how impossible it is to confront head on the forces behind man's processing of his environment. Such a confrontation sometimes diverts, occasionally delays, and often distorts the processing; but a total cessation it has yet to work. As for repining, the literature is full of it, some quite poetic and beautiful; but if it is a lament, the pity lies in having to deliver it, and if it is exhortation, it, too, should be integrated into a program for attaining full realization of what it is exactly man has been, and is, doing.

The times in which such realization could be ignored are now over for all except the determinedly ignorant; and if serious consequences are to be avoided or even minimized, those with that sort of ignorance had better decrease in number and be moved out of positions of authority. A change must take place, one that will bring together on the public level of control through force and social pressure all the disciplines capable of affecting this environment: biological, physical, technical, economic, political, and moral. In brief, it is the time for a moderation foreign to man's tradition.

law as the
means to the end

The cultural phenomenon called law is not the only power in the scheme for moderating man's impact on his environment. No one discipline or craft is. Law itself may not even be coequal with what it is coordinating. Aside from its techniques for seeking to accomplish ends over which various parties are bitter adversaries, law has little else to offer. Its substance must come from outside the law; and it is scarcely conceivable apart from the contenders with whom it deals but with which law ought not to be confused.

Law is a bailiff for the ruling power of the moment, lending to that power its authority. Like any obedient bailiff, it wants to be told by the present powers (or, if for any reason they can utter no commands, then by the movers of some impending power) precisely what to do. Without such fresh commands the law will merely continue to pursue, with steadily less relevance to anything except rote tradition, whatever last orders were given it, however inappropriate altered circumstances have made them.

The fault of environmental failure does not lie in the legal process but in those who cannot or will not use it for better purpose. As a process, law is in every way neutral and will respond to its controllers with whatever they seek to perform. This is not to excuse lawyers from culpability nor to say that any use of legal process— even nonuse—will lack effect. It is only to point out that law has concepts and skills anyone can use, whatever the ultimate purpose or the consequence stemming from the very absence of purpose.

The means presently exist for controlling the environment for an outcome other than the destruction of its life-sustaining properties. Economics can work our model showing the interaction of all events in terms of a cost-benefit ratio. Ecology has increased knowledge to keep up balances between life forms. Politics has institutions capable of reflecting, making operative, and regulating conflicting constituencies concerned in imposing demands upon the human environment. Technology has crafts available to supervise in detail whatever is done anywhere within the ecumene, man's world-wide household. And law has now available the procedures for translating all this into publicly effective levels of action through whose mechanisms the demands of man could be controlled so as to produce an environment able to sustain what is required of it over a future of indeterminate length.

The knowledge is currently available; and tentatively being used. Unfortunately, all those skills could be used just to accelerate the consumption of whatever is viable in the environment. Knowledge has a fascination requiring application; but the results are more various than the users often anticipated. Yet whatever the danger, knowledge and aggressive human demands upon the environment keep thrusting forward with the imperiousness of the irresistible; and some general design for control must absolutely be set up within the next generation.

Technically, legally, stabilization can be accomplished. What is needed from now on is the will to make the decision to undertake the full extent of what such a choice means for change. Still, if the decision is not made in that preserving direction so that some or all of the dire predictions come true by the year 2000 or shortly thereafter, the reason will not lie in any flaw in man's inventive abilities, but in a psyche that has been unable to make the necessary decision, or effectively use its inventive ability, or apply what had been developed as techniques for preserving life. The choice will be made very soon; and rational excuses no longer exist for it to be made in any direction other than man's full assumption of the responsibility for his environment. It is, after all, the goal toward which everything man has done has trended since his emergence as a separate nature. Perhaps he will see it as marking his course from merger with nature to merger with divinity; but however it is seen, man thrusts away his responsibility at peril of extinction.

REFERENCES

Durward Allen, *Our Wildlife Legacy,* 2nd ed., New York: Funk & Wagnalls, 1962.

Sigmund von Ciriacy-Wantrup, *Resource Conservation: Economics and Politics,* 2nd ed., Berkeley: University of California Press, 1963.

René Dubos, *So Human an Animal,* New York: Scribner, 1968.

Loren Eiseley, *The Firmament of Time,* New York: Atheneum Publishers, 1960.

Eugene P. Odum, *Ecology,* New York: Holt, Rinehart and Winston, 1963.

Robert Rienow and Leona Train Rienow, *Moment in the Sun: A Report on the Deteriorating Quality of the American Environment,* New York: Dial Press, 1967.

Paul Shepard, *Man in the Landscape: A Historic View of the Esthetics of Nature,* New York: Knopf, 1967.

William Vogt, *Road to Survival,* New York: Sloane, 1948.

Erich W. Zimmerman, *Introduction to World Resources* (Henry Hunker, ed.), New York: Harper & Row, 1964.

2
law
and
environmental
use

the subordinate role of law

Law is a technique for the ordered accomplishment of social and economic purposes. The best legal technique generally is judged to be the procedure that allows these ends to be most quickly reached with a minimum of investment in energy and capital. The fact that there may be other consequences than those initially intended is not regarded as any judgment on the law. The untoward side effects are no part of the judgment passed on the law, nor should they be.

This, at least, is the traditional view; and, however blandly it smooths over the disasters occurring as unpredicted by-products, this interpretation is not improper for the intermediate stages for attaining some result. After all, law primarily serves the major interests dominating the culture and, in a sophisticated culture, the major concerns are those of wealth and power. They are concerns stressing the ability of the culture's resource base to produce; and the legal system will be a vehicle for that productivity.

The consequential meaning of such a relationship is the preoccupation of the law with means of exploitation and ways of allocating its profit. The gathering of taxes for the support of the army, the maintenance of a state apparatus, or the distribution of charity requires a high extraction of wealth from the resource base. The most kindly of kings would still require the collection of taxes; and such a collection, whether in cash, kind, or services, would have to come from the exploitation of the environment even in the good kingdom.

It has been pointed out that the rapid development of midwestern American cities in the late nineteenth century was at the expense of the forests of the north central states. These cities were built of pine and poplar, rapidly and cheaply, as a softwood subsidy. The rich hardwoods that originally had stood on the site of future cities were not used to build them. The massive stands of oak, walnut, ash, and wild cherry were cut down, piled into huge heaps, and burned. The frontier newspaper accounts of the size of the logs, the height of the piles, the intensity of the fires, and the number of days they burned were awesome to the men who wrote them and pathetic to those who now read them. The dark forests were first frightening, then oppressive, later a nuisance, and finally only a memory.

The clearance of the hardwood forests made a place for the rapid growth of agriculture and city life. But when the time came to build cities, there were insufficient local woods with which to work. Brick and stone might have been used, but they would have meant a slower, more expensive, more crowded mode of life; and the developers were not interested. Instead, what was wanted was the spaciously laid out city with wide streets and roomy lots and detached houses sitting each in its own garden. Clapboarded, painted, in shady grounds, this was to be the dwelling for the growing middle class. And the numbers able to afford such homes were to be enlarged by the cheap price of soft timber. The basis of what was to become the typical middle-class American home was laid at the expense of the great northern forests. Lumbermen chewed their way without pause from Maine right through to Oregon. For them the plains were just a swallow between bites.

the business
of processing
the environment

In order to do all this, a great deal of business had to be organized. A network had to be established to raft the logs out in giant booms, to cut them into millions of board feet of planks and studs, to carry them by rail to the yards, and to deliver the product to one development builder after another. Temporary camps and towns had to be built in the lumbering regions, labor recruited, and new techniques for rapid construction worked out.

Jerry-building came into its own era in the United States after the Civil War. The rate at which new towns or subdivisions for existing towns were thrown up was nothing short of amazing. Early photographs often show structures in the framework stage of building for as far as the camera could see. So cheap a material was wood that sidewalks, gutters, dams, sluices, and other quickly deteriorated structures were made entirely out of un-painted, untreated pieces.

In the faded old photos what often seems a dirt street will show peeking out under the packed earth the nar-rowly laid boards of a plank road. The easiest way to get a smooth traveling surface and to counter the voracious mud was to cut down some thousands of trees and slice them into planks for road-building. It was less extrava-gant than the earlier corduroy which had been built by laying the logs themselves side by side without regard for how many planks could have been found in each of the logs so casually flung into the roadway.

So that all this might be done as cheaply as possible, large amounts of capital were required and considerable credit. The United States was a debtor nation, dependent upon foreign investments or what could be earned from overseas trade; and any means that could avoid expend-ing cash from either was favored. This put pressure be-hind a policy of quick and extensive mobilization of the resources, and this pressure was intensified by the chronic shortage of labor throughout the nineteenth cen-tury. Other countries might create capital from the labor of their people, but the American system took capital from natural wealth.

The job of the law in this development was not directly related to natural resources. The institution of the corporation, limited liability, security instruments on extended credit, or insured risks was each vital to the quickening of processes that strengthened the urban-industrial development running through the nineteenth and into the twentieth century. The forests of the north central states could not have been cut, carried a thousand or more miles away, and flung up to make the new wooden cities of the plains without such legal devices. The legal routines were as integral to these events as the national market or the industrial revolution. What had to be sacrificed in this adjustment to rapidly changing conditions were elements of the resource base; and these were fed into the process without much regard for what might be irretrievably lost.

laws in a
period of exploitation

Law could only respond to this attitude. In an economy essentially concerned with exploitation, where the values were those of production and high investment return, the law could scarcely do otherwise, though many laws were passed that at first appearance seem designed to conserve the environment. Closer inspection, however, showed this to be an incidental result, perhaps not even peripherally intended.

The dumping into rivers of lumber wastes was commonly prohibited. This would seem to show a desire to protect water quality but actually it was to protect the industry against itself. So cheap was wood that scraps and fragments were lightly discarded into the nearest creek to be swept away by the water. These were the same streams needed to carry the logs to the mills and the lumber away from them to the railhead or market. Careless operators, heedless of the streams' capacity to bear such a burden of waste, jammed the channels with trash to the degree that, if not prevented, would have risked the life of the entire industry.

The same was true of statutes barring dumping by slaughter houses, boneyards, leather curers, paper mills, and similar conversion industries. Today, when so many wastes can be used to make by-products, or else reduced in quantity by more economical techniques of manufacture, it is difficult to conceive of the volume of what was discarded. The problem of solid waste and of an economy risking its suffocation in what it discards is not new. It is inherent in the success of the industrial society. The greater the affluence produced or the cheaper the commodities involved in manufacturing, the greater the quantity of throwaways.

The difference between what the nineteenth century had as refuse and what makes up the solid waste in the late twentieth century is in the ease of what is called degradability. Residues from living organisms decay and disappear sooner than glass or metals, and it is these latter substances that are increasingly available for junk. What is piling up today promises to be around far longer than what cluttered the river beds and municipal environs a century ago.

The refuse of the past, however, was bad enough. "White water" at one time did not mean rapids but a stream choked with pulp unused at a paper mill. Canneries could fill a stream from bank to bank with pumpkin rind or pea pods, while butchers would hurl most of the carcass of a beef into the creek for disposal. Considering the importance even small streams then had for navigation and for turning mill wheels, such practices could only hurt industry. Perhaps advancing prices and changing techniques were more important in altering this sort of wastefulness. The first pipelines, for example, appeared in western Pennsylvania in the mid-1860s because the oil field operations were filling in the very backwaters used to barge out the petroleum. Under circumstances like these the prohibiting statutes were not for the help of nature but for the aid of the very industries that had to moderate their dumping of waste. It was business, not the natural resource, that was meant to be guarded by the intervention of law.

*transferring
the resource burden*

The common practice generally has been to transfer the burden imposed by changing demands from one part of the environment to another; and this was especially true for industrial waste. In the mid-seventeenth century a royal official was appointed to pick carrion from the Thames and borough ordinances were passed penalizing the throwing of trash in waters within a town. Perhaps the silting up of some of the smaller English harbors made their town councils economically sensitive to dumpers of junk capable of accumulation on the harbor floor. But most of the pre-nineteenth-century legislation seems preoccupied with simply preserving the amenities: No one wants the bloated remnants of the knacker's yard swirling below his river view.

The nineteenth century, however, found something worse than a matter of amenity presenting itself. In the 1830s Parliament in the old palace at Westminster found the stench rising from the Thames so intense that it either had to adjourn or hang sodden canvas soaked in aromatics to cut off the vapor from the river. It was the result of the nineteenth-century decision to use water as the prime waste receptor.

In the Middle Ages, sewers were a rarity. Instead, waste was removed by wagon to dumps outside the walls. In poorer districts there was accumulation, and some cities used their moats for deposit of trash or just flung it over the town wall. But these were exceptions. Despite popular myth to the contrary, the average medieval town was cleaner than its sucessor during the eighteenth century's Age of Reason or the nineteenth century's Industrial Revolution. The smaller populations, simpler technology, and more compact size in actual space covered made it possible to dispose of waste by haulage and land-fill. What destroyed this option was the concentration of greater populations in the cities, the appearance of industries continuously producing off-fall, and an urban sprawl that bankrupted scavengers be-

cause of hauling distances. By the early nineteenth century it looked as if the cities of the new industrial age
might sink under their own filth.

The salvation which appeared at that time was the re-
discovery of the hydraulic principle. It required the
small-bore, smoothly tiled, terra cotta conduit, which was
cheap, easy to install, and required little maintenance.
With the new sewer pipe, self-cleansed by hydraulics,
there was every reason to dump down the drain whatever
could be reduced to flowable state. The cities were
cleansed at the expense of their receiving waters; and
the price of city living on a modern, late-nineteenth-cen-
tury scale was the reduction of some luckless rivers to
the rank of open sewers.

It was a community decision, which the law initially
could only assist. Sewer districts were rapidly organized
so that city life could become hygienic. Reformers enthu-
siastically pushed their construction for every class and
every district. The Brontë sisters interrupted their dark
visions in poetry and novel long enough to call for public
sewer construction. A decision had been made to get rid
of one problem by trading it off for another problem,
which would not enter an acute phase till generations
later.

municipal consequences
of resource trade-offs

The law's function was to make the trade-off possible by
developing new institutions of local government such as
sewer commissioners, credit devices such as the improvement bond, and fiscal measures such as the special
assessments for improvements. At a time of severe capital shortage and general municipal corruption, it seemed
essential to earmark funds exactly for the purposes for
which they were to be spent, to finance the work as
nearly as possible from payments drawn from those particularly benefited, and to put persons in charge whose
duty and responsibility could be easily identified.

The effect on municipal life was profound. Cities prior
to this time had been loose federations of precincts (the
secular replacement for the old parish) and wards. This

was where government actually took place, with each
alderman being chief executive of his ward and with
boards of health existing in each precinct and street
commissioners in each ward. Councilmen met as ambas-
sadors at the city level to negotiate local interests.

The financial requirements of the new industrial economy for publicly financed infrastructure to support the
growing system of private enterprise literally exploded
this cosy world of neighborhoods and democracy. Sewers, paved streets, lighting, police and fire protection,
schools, dumps, hospitals, and fire and health codes
were all needs previously either not required or else not
very much so. The new sewers alone would have been
enough to wreck the old system. Larger credit was
needed than a single ward, much less a precinct, could
supply. Areas, still undeveloped and thus without improved property to put up as security, had acute needs
for sewerage for booming industry and population. And if
the sewers were to function efficiently, they had to do it
as a municipality-wide trunk system.

Power and fiscal authority passed directly to City Hall,
where new departments were formed around specific
functions: sewers, streets, health, schools, and so forth.
They were sustained partly out of the general property
tax but, insofar as possible, special assessments were
used as their financial support. If new sewers were to be
built, a temporary levy was imposed, to be used only for
that purpose and terminated when the sewer was fin-
ished. If money had to be borrowed, a mortgage was imposed on the property to be benefited, bonds were se-
cured by this mortgage and sold to investors, and a
special assessment was imposed to be collected from
the benefited property or a city-wide fund composed of
merging local programs in order to pay the interest on
the bonds and retire them when due.

At a later date, when the law had conceived of the
sewer city (a vision of the municipality as existing only
as a sewerage system), the joint sewer district (in which
cities and residents outside cities could pool both physical problems and financial resources), and the sewer authority (under which an autonomous agency handles

wastes for an entire region), it was possible to improve the finance methods worked out by the coordinated nineteenth-century cities. Unfortunately, the new techniques move even further away from democratic control by those being served. In addition credit and taxes tend to lose their earmarkings, the specificity of cash allocations gets blurred, and the location of executive responsibility becomes hard to trace. But that lay in the future, beyond the generation of the lawyers who had to develop the legal means which aided the swift expansion of the urban-industrial revolution in the nineteenth century.

The lawyer's job, when only one instance is selected as an example, was to make the transition possible from one form of waste disposal (land-fill) to another (waterborne); and if stream quality was a casualty, the law could worry about it no more than the community did. When internal navigation went into decline after the Civil War under the impact of rail competition, the last obvious reason to keep rivers clean seemed ended. American cities, for the most part, firmly turned their backsides to their rivers and made terms like "waterfront" or "the levee" expressions of decadence and blight.

environmental indifference in an age of exploitation

The few nineteenth-century efforts to deal with water quality for its own sake, however tentative, came to nothing. Sir Edwin Chadwick, the guiding force in the 1840s of the British General Board of Health, found himself driven from office when he tried to push for action in this area. At a time when water-borne diseases such as cholera and typhoid were at unprecedented levels, there was little public interest in such preventatives as sand filtration of water (known to be effective since 1829) or exclusion of raw sewage from supplies of drinking water (shown by Dr. John Snow in 1849 to be a means of stopping cholera). But the public preferred to dismiss officials who tried to act along those lines rather than transfer scarce capital, otherwise capable of doubling itself in the normal course of investment every five years, into water and sewer projects promising slight cash return.

The same was true in the United States where a National Board of Health had a brief career around the administration of Rutherford B. Hayes. Its most lasting accomplishment was the development by Dr. John Billings of the punched card for the purpose of keeping records. Another age, however, got the advantage of that invention; and the agency for which it had been made disappeared.

The story at the state level was about the same. The Civil War experience did produce the formation of central state administrative agencies organized to accomplish particular functions of fairly narrow scope like state boards of health, fish and game commissions, and park wardens. Poorly funded, staffed largely by volunteers, enjoying scant public support, often compared to the servants of Old Europe's tyrants from whom free Americans had fled, they were the first feeble beginning in a natural resource program that could be more than governmental limitation upon the right of industries, skills, classes, and regions from committing suicide.

Modest they certainly were, and put down with severity whenever they sought to be more. The brief history of the Wisconsin State Committee on Water Supply in the late 1870s will suffice as an example. It had been set up by the newly formed Board of Health to determine the healthfulness of the state's supply of drinking water. In a day before Pasteur had discovered bacteria, the only test of taintedness was for organic matter, based on the theory that a quick way to spread a disease was to flush the victims' dejecta into the drinking supply. So hot was the issue that the professor of chemistry at the state university refused to make the survey, giving as his reason that a chemical scholar of his worth could not be expected to conduct "mere" tests. A high school principal and chemistry teacher was finally found to volunteer; and his report showed there was scarcely a safe source of water in the state. In the ensuing uproar he was fired from his jobs, run out of town, and given later employment through the compassion of physicians on the board who realized, too late, what they had asked of him. The

committee was abolished; and the board avoided a similar fate by only the most abject apology, accompanied by
a promise never to err again.

Wisconsin was not going to tolerate a report from a
state agency casting doubt on the safety of the water
supply. The doubt was not denied. But the stating of
such a doubt was a culpable offense, only comparatively
less so than proposing that anything should be done
other than suppressing the doubters. It was not a climate, in short, congenial to any reform in current styles
of natural resource use.

The law reflects such community views as are able to
struggle to prominence and find sufficient support in the
contemporary power structure. At the very time in the
United States, for example, when cutting in the forests
was moving into the frenzied pace that was to remain
typical through the 1920s, voices were raised to express
alarm. In 1867 a committee of the Wisconsin Legislature
urged a policy of rotating the planting and cutting of
hardwoods. It was rejected as "uneconomic" on several
grounds: There would never be a shortage in the natural
supply; the delay in harvest time of up to a hundred
years from planting was too long; and hardwoods were
too difficult to encourage artificially. At the same instant
they believed that there would never be a lack of hardwoods to cut; that, once cut, hardwoods would not replace themselves; and that any return from reforestation
required too long a delay. No one seems to have seen
the flaw in the reasoning.

prolonging the
chance at exploitation

The economic rationalists often prefer the arguments Dugald Stewart used in 1791 to persuade the British to
cease the Elizabethan program for planting oaks: The
ground could be put to a higher cash-return use; oaks
took too long to mature; and oaken timbers could always
be imported from Illyria. Demands in the nineteenth century, which exceeded any historic figures Stewart had
available, destroyed Illyria's oaks; and similar influences
were at work in the forests of the United States at the

same time. Because of poor cutting practices, as many trees were burned as were cut by American lumbermen; and, as far as forest effect was concerned, the figures for cutting must be doubled, at a minimum, in order to calculate board feet removed from the living environment as the immediate result of cutting programs. This excludes from the figures the influence of disease, climate, erosion, and animal predators on the forests so gravely weakened by such lumbering programs.

Unlike the German princelings and their imitators, both England and the United States have turned their forest resources over to the actions of the unconstrained market. The German nobility, foreseeing only an endless vista stretching ahead of their dynasties, had been concerned with their financial maintenance. Not having industry then available for investment, they looked to their lands for this sustenance; and in the eighteenth century they had begun a program of replanting trees cut so that, through rotation, their dynastic forests would maintain a constant size and steady cash earnings for them.

The idea may have derived from Spanish law, which required that a tree be planted for every one cut, a requirement extended to the Spanish Indies in the 1550s. But this was a general law, imposed by some worried bureaucrat at court and subject to evasion. What the northern European nobility did was undertaken in order to profit themselves and to provide an economic base for their never-ending families. For this purpose they hired foresters, financed the beginnings of a science of forestry, improved both timber stands and single species, maintained a base for a wide range of wood-using industries, and kept up a stable economy for workers in forest areas. It was selfish and authoritarian; it kept viable a noble caste in the region until recently; it made possible the successful timber trusts in Latvia (including the production of "Riga modern" furniture) and Prussia (as presently divided among the U.S.S.R., Poland, and East Germany); and it showed the world that indefinitely sustained yields of high rate and high quality for timber were possible. Whatever the motive, the result was grand.

The news of such operations had become well known in Wisconsin, with its German, Scandinavian, and Baltic immigrants, at an early date; but not until 1867 was the knowledge revealed at an official level, and the first American state's forest was not founded until 1878. Looking backward, it is sad to realize that if rotation of hardwood forests had been begun in Wisconsin at that time, the first yields would have appeared in the 1920s, and they would now be in a peak of production that proper care could sustain almost indefinitely. If one generation could have gratitude for a predecessor, our generation should have had it for the wisdom of men who would have founded a rotating hardwood forestry policy in the very midst of a frantically exploding timber market. It was not to be, however. Those holding such views, whatever their wisdom, had too little power to prevail against the opinions and special interests of their times.

Instead, that generation had to concentrate in matters of forest conservancy along the more negative line of locking away whatever it could from the cutters. In 1864 Yosemite and in 1871 Yellowstone were set aside as unique treasures. They were not yet true parks, but they had been preserved until such time as a later age could make parks of them. In 1873 Congress passed the Timber Culture Act, giving advantages to settlers who would keep in timber 40 out of every 120 acres. In 1878 Carl Schurz, the first Secretary of the Interior interested in conservation, called for setting aside at least some of the redwoods in a preserve free of cutting; and in 1891 Congress authorized the President to set aside certain public lands as forests. The ones first selected by President Harrison were little more then designated, being akin in this regard to the New York state forests which an 1894 constitutional amendment had put outside the reach of cutting for any reason whatsoever. The federal forestry officials in the Department of Agriculture, few as they were, had been expected from their first appearance in 1876 to count trees and not to run a lumber program. The first wardens in the General Land Office were at the same time no more than inadequate custodians.

Those concerned with forest conservation in the United States in the nineteenth century had to be satis-

fied with running a rescue mission. Not until Gifford Pin-
chot began his work in the 1890s did a successful force
appear who could see the possibilities of the American
forests for indefinitely sustained yields. The best American law could do in the nineteenth century was to save a
few areas. Only at a later time could the legal system go
beyond that point and respond with legal changes capable of starting self-sustaining forests.

law and wilderness preservation

Indeed, the course of development may now have
evolved in the twentieth century into a third stage, when
public monies will be laid out for the active preservation
of wilderness areas. In this kind of zone, not only would
the sustained-yield method of tree rotation be disal-
lowed, but so also would the multiple-purpose forest concept. Such areas would exclude all visitors except those
there for serious study and prepared to move across the
land with minimal disturbance. Wilderness regions will
never have much size; and even should their creation
enjoy enthusiastic support, they can have only a limited
and diminishing scope. The power is simply lacking on a
globe so integrated that penguins have DDT in their tissues. This kind of impact can only increase. Yet insofar
as there is an effectively expressed community desire to
recognize wilderness preservation, the law has as good
means to help attain that end as it has to assist in wiping
out the last vestiges of wildlife.

In one sense this is a very ancient function of the law.
The idea of the royal demesne operated somewhat like
the modern multipurpose forest and sometimes like a wilderness area. As a legal concept, it may stem from the
forests of ancient Rome, which were held directly under
the title of the republic and were managed by commissioners who supervised cutting for state building projects. With further conquest the institution brought major
imperial forests to Iberia, the Balkans, and northwest Africa. This is not to say that the emperors did not deed off
large tracts to veterans or generals in order to curry

favor with important supporting groups and individuals. Some of the most thorough deforestation, with subsequent soil erosion and loss of water retention, took place on imperial lands used as bounty for veterans. The Roman forests, whether republican or imperial, only prolonged the existence of commercially valuable trees. Trees lasted as commercial spoil in southern Italy and Sicily from the arrival of the Greek settlers about 700 B.C. until the Napoleonic wars. Two thousand years of cutting at last had removed temptation; and the lasting impact of Roman forestry lay not in keeping up the resource of trees but in providing the legal institution of a forest preserve.

The English royal demesne had an importance as valuable to the Crown as the imperial forests had for the emperor, with the king issuing a special set of laws for the forest. Persons living or coming within the demesne were subject to this law; and at a time when the king's command rarely could penetrate the feudal system to fall directly on either freeman or serf, the forest was the most extensive area within which the royal presence was immediately felt. The king's servants stopped or punished encroachments on the forest, ranging from the petty depredations of charcoal burners in the deep woods to noble lords engrossing chunks of the king's demesne along the forest's rim. Both types were constant; both in the long run were fatal to the forest; and neither is easy to weigh as to relative worth in extinguishing the forest. But together, their power cannot be denied; and between the nether and upper millstones, the royal forests were ground to bits.

Yet until that took place, the Crown fought hard to maintain in full the royal demesne. Cutting trees and underbrush, lopping branches, picking up fallen limbs, cutting turf, or taking fish or game were all forbidden or severely limited unless a fee were paid. They were not popular laws and bore harshly on the lower classes, who often needed to supplement from the forest what their own holdings provided.

Unpopular as the royal demesne was with the lower orders, it was no more acceptable to their social betters.

The emigrants to the British North American colonies, whatever their social origins at home, were to fight the transplanting of the concept. In England itself the effective opposition came from the upper classes in the countryside. They had both the political and economic means to profit from the exploitation of the demesne. When the effort had succeeded by the end of the eighteenth century, the royal demesne was a remnant, to be deeded to the country by the dynasty in return for an annual pension.

Still, while it lasted, the effect on resources seems to have been substantial. Game was a part of the English diet until 1725; charcoal remained the chief fuel until after 1800; the country remained heavily forested until late Tudor times, pit props for English mines were supplied by forests in the United Kingdom until 1880; builders did not have to rely on the Baltic timber trade until the nineteenth century; and huge logs were available for the fireplaces of the great country houses until early in the present century. The medieval English kings were purely selfish in their exclusive claims on the forest, yet the side effect of that exclusion was the prolonging of the use of what was protected by this policy. Conservation was nowhere in those royal minds, but a kind of conservation was the consequence.

risks of predicting
legal impact
on the environment

In conservation law the motives are often mixed ones; and consequences that produce the least disturbance in the environment are sometimes the product of purposes quite selfish, while noble purposes bring out most unanticipated results. After all, it was reformers gathered around Theodore Roosevelt who inaugurated the high dam-great reservoir programs that became common to the twentieth century. They had been worried over the failure of the Desert Lands Act of 1877 and the Carey Act of 1894 to introduce irrigation, concerned over increasing desiccation, bothered about dire predictions of food shortage, and anxious to extend settlement in the empty Southwest. Prior to this century, even the most magnificent hydraulic civilizations of the past had been compelled to perform without great open reservoirs. But the technology had been lacking to build the high dams that the Bureau of Reclamation began to construct after 1902. First meant to aid irrigation, their uses were soon extended by other reformers to producing hydropower and controlling floods. These required still larger heads of water; and with the best of motives the entire legal-economic-political complex was mobilized to produce massive interventions in the environment.

The work done so effectively by these well-minded people has proven most upsetting to many later conservationists. The fears of the naturalist John Muir, who from at least 1909 was opposed to the new high dams, turned out fully merited. The intervention has been about as severe as his worst predictions; and what makes this bad is the shortage of many remaining wild resources, an unfortunate insistence that every portion of nature be judged by its comparative ability to produce a cash flow, and a reluctance to realize that the changes produced have been profound, rarely foreseen, often unfortunate, and perhaps irreversible. Predicting the impact of legal programs on the environment is a risky business and certainly its prediction is not always possible for those initiating such programs.

Law, of course, can contribute directly to sustaining a stable use of resource; and the maintenance of soil richness is an example of a project that has fulfilled its promise. Too many believe that the law's concern with soil began with H. H. Bennett's work in creating the United States Soil Conservation Service in the 1930s or, at the earliest, the appointment in 1792 as secretary of the British Board of Agriculture of Arthur Young, the Father of Scientific Agriculture. But this is not true, if the meaning of law is given a sufficiently wide scope. The law's interest in the richness of soil goes back to the Middle Ages in western Europe and the seasonal meetings of the lord of the manor with his tenants who held land of him in servile tenure.

There was considerably more to the age of chivalry than knightly tournaments, not the least important of which was the manorial system on which the economy was organized. Ideally, the country was divided into these manors, each with its mansion house, its fields, its local industries, its tenants, and its dependent village. Basically a subsistence economy, producing whatever was needed within the village and having only a small surplus for market, the manor was highly static and non-commercial in character. As a result, customs grew up slowly that were as binding on the lord of the manor as they were on his tenants. They related to a common use of resources, such as gleaning fields, extracting peat from the bogs, pasturage over certain lands at certain seasons; and they were as valuable to the tenants as the lord's rights were to him to hunt over the whole estate, make the tenants grind at his mill or cure at his tannery, charge a fee for fishing, or enjoy a monopoly in dovecots and beehives. The arrival of a cash economy was to smash this brittle compromise into bits; but in the interval it functioned well enough for both sides to the bargain to cling to it, and for the tenants to part from it with great reluctance.

As custom demanded, the lord met with his chief tenants. This composed the manorial court and the custom it dispensed was manorial law. Disputes were settled, the profits of the customs were accounted for, and the fields were reassigned. At its best, the manorial court operated like its model, the court of a great suzerein and his vassals, with the humble tenants replacing their betters in the decision-making. At its worst, of course, it was only cruel charade; and at a later period, with the lord's introduction of trained lawyers and what was called manorial equity, it became the scene for the suppression of the tenants' customary rights. Yet when they worked well, manorial courts with their customs were important for resource use control, and their most significant jurisdiction lay in dividing up the land each year.

At a time when fertilization was practically unknown, the best means of keeping up the richness of the soil was to allow the land to lie fallow and to rotate the production of certain crops which, experience had shown, sustained the soil's capacity. Since many tenant families had to share in the total production, it was not practical to make a permanent assignment of land to a family. Instead, the manorial court made new assignments each year, withdrawing some of the land for fallowing and ordering particular crops to be raised on the land assigned.

Because little of the product went to market for cash sale and nearly all was used on the manor, there was little reason to complain whatever the allocation of fields or crops. There was neither technology to increase production nor a market to which such increase might have gone, so that there was no reason for individual initiative. Until new crops, new techniques, and new markets appeared (almost simultaneously about the time of Columbus' voyages), there was no reason for any farmer to seek permanent possession of any particular tract or for any lord to be very aggressive in bringing all the resources of an area under his single title. Under the market and technical conditions of the time the old manors acted as a brake upon resource use and as a means of controlling the working of the soil so as to prolong its wealth. Whenever the manor courts met, their decisions were important to the natural environment; and when they ceased to meet, their passing marked a definite alteration in the level of resource demand and the role law would play in it.

This institution was not a force for resource conservation in itself. What was the effective braking power was the static mode of medieval life. With its lack of markets, its scanty trade, the absence of sufficient media of exchange, its deflation of the coinage, the chronic imbalance of trade with Asia, the inability to move vertically in the class structure, the tying of the people to their localities, there were far more important conservative influences than manorial law for holding back exploitation of resources. The incentive was missing for aggressive actions mining resources.

However, this was a transitory phase in European history. Markets revived, stimulating production for the market rather than for mere subsistence. The return of markets reproduced the need for speciality in trades, with a resulting strengthening of a return to a money exchange economy. The presence of money provoked movements of population and enabled individuals over several generations to move sharply upward in the social scale. The discovery of the New World brought a flood of gold to the economy which inaugurated the inflationary spiral marking the world since 1500. The new trade and even newer technology began to close off Asia's traditional favorable balance until by the eighteenth century it had reached the unfavorable level where it since has remained.

The eleventh century A.D. had found the European continent stable, as economically and socially stationary as such a volatile area could expect to be, with as small a demand on its resource base as it has had since Greece and Rome extended the requirements of an urban-commercial civilization from western Asia to the bulk of Europe. But every century after that has found less stability. The conditions that had produced such small resource demands were being eaten away by the rise, once again, of urban-commercial society, with all of its market demands; and this progressive movement from stability to constant economic movement was enhanced by the Industrial Revolution. After that, what before might have been expected to exert a conserving influence became a pressure for deeper or more extensive change.

Even where ancient elements hung on into the new era, they were not any longer preserving of resources. The presence of market influence and a cash economy, seeping in everywhere, assured such a change. The old forms became merely additional competitors in the market, doomed competitors even though hanging on in parts of Europe until the twentieth century. They were inefficient competitors from the angle of income production; and like any economic unit in such a situation, they were driven to tricks and evasions for survival which made them abusers of the very resources—soil, grass, trees, wildlife—that they had once protected.

In this instance the disappearance of their old legal

means of expression intensified the harmful effect. The day of manorial courts and the importance of manorial custom were over in England by the fifteenth century. Attempts in other parts of Europe to revive them were oppressive to peasants and resources alike. There could be no turning back to premarket forms in a market economy. The only effect could be to make these revivals cruel, stupid, and unbearable diseconomies, important only for helping to precipitate rural revolt. What were sadly lacking were not the old manorial customs and courts, but a replacement for them that would take account of the changes that had occurred.

Once the static condition of Europe had been put in motion and a premium placed on resource exploitation rather than preservation, the institutions of the Middle Ages had nothing to offer. This was true not only of the assembly of his tenants by the lord of the manor into his manorial court, but equally so of the royal demesne of the forest, the royal prerogative over fish, game, and water, or the royal right to forfeit feudal possessions because of their holders having encroached on the royal interest. None of these fitted the certainty, the specificity, or the extent of ownership required under the changed conditions. Instead, they served as hindrances that in their hindering had no redeeming function so far as resource preservation was concerned. Once the cash nexus had been established as holding the economy together and as the essential test for wealth and power, the incentive was introduced for racking everything out of land that was going to be only briefly under one's control. The restraining hand was not to be found in worn-out forms, drained by time and changed conditions of all substance.

the long-standing
concern of law
with the environment

However, although different times demand different legal techniques, the point of the medieval European experience is that there exists an ancient history for the law's concern with preserving resources as well as with their exploitation. The fact that peculiar social conditions of the Middle Ages caused the law to so operate is no more relevant than that different pressures peculiar to the age of the Industrial Revolution made the nineteenth century's legal forms predominantly helpful in furthering resource exploitation. Law can only respond to the uses to which it is put; and the dominant impulses of the time must determine those uses.

When the concern for the environment and the rapidity of demands made upon its resources began to be expressed in the late nineteenth century, that concern had to invent its own means of making itself effective. Ancient examples might inspire but they could not formulate solutions. Because of this necessity to be inventive, a good deal of stumbling experimentation was inevitable. But an occasional blunder in seeking new control devices is far superior than either lack of control or a use of worn-out inherited techniques.

Since the turn of the present century, the law has tried out a great many new control devices. In a time of exploding technological change, nothing less could be expected. The problem, clearly, is not that the law has been too experimental but rather that technology and rising demand have outpaced the rate of the law's ability to create control measures capable of bringing both into balance with the resources on which all human enterprise depends. There is a gap between the existing and the needed condition which the law has failed to close; and in the filling of that gap lies the difference between the survival and the demise of the kind of urban-industrial civilization that has spread over the entire world since the eighteenth century.

Because of the need to close this gap, it is beginning to appear as if the year 2000 might mark the kind of fearful watershed soothsayers foretold for the year A.D. 1000, except that this time the dire words lie in science or technology rather than in mysticism or the black arts. The essential difference, also, between the two is that this time the fulfillment lies more in Man's hands than in Fate's. The only issue is whether the direness in the new prophecies will be fulfilled or avoided, although whichever the outcome, law will have been its help along the way.

REFERENCES

Walter Firey, *Man, Mind, and Land: A Theory of Resource Use,* New York: Free Press, 1960.

Michael Frome, *Whose Woods These Are: The Story of the National Forests,* Garden City, N.Y.: Doubleday, 1962.

James Willard Hurst, *Law and Economic Growth: The Legal History of the Lumber Industry in Wisconsin, 1836–1915,* Cambridge, Mass.: Belknap Press, 1964.

Robert S. Kerr, *Land, Wood, and Water* (M. Stephenson and T. Coffin, eds.), New York: Macfadden Capitol Hill Books, 1963.

James A. Lake, *Law and Mineral Wealth: The Legal Profile of the Wisconsin Mining Industry,* Madison: University of Wisconsin Press, 1962.

Roscoe A. Martin and others, *Decisions in Syracuse: A Metropolitan Action Study,* Garden City, N.Y.: Anchor Books, 1965.

Earl Finbar Murphy, *Water Purity: A Study in Legal Control of Natural Resources,* Madison: University of Wisconsin Press, 1961.

Anthony Scott, *Natural Resources: The Economics of Conservation,* Toronto, Canada: University of Toronto Press, 1955.

Samuel W. Tait, Jr., *The Wildcatters: An Informal History of Oil Hunting in America,* Princeton: Princeton University Press, 1946.

3

changing
man's
traditions
about nature

A common expression exists that there is nothing new under the sun. This is particularly appealing to anyone with a historical bias. Very often historical example is called upon to show how much better affairs were once managed, or to indicate how hopeless a certain approach once proved, or to justify some present method because of its ancient antecedents. It is the use of history as dogma, approving or condemning exclusively in terms of what has been done previously in a situation supposedly the same.

This is not quite the equivalent of researching the past for its accumulated experiences. To look at the past for assistance is not like going back to it to receive commands, but examining critically whatever is there to be found. It is pitiful to be presently imprisoned in a set of inherited ideas that distort the reality out of which they were formed. But it is self-handicapping never to look back. Rejection of the past as an established cultural trait is a prison just as confining as worshiping the past. Only instead of shutting up the present among the relics of a dead past, it would enclose it in the ever-busy moment. At one point in Western cultural history, probably the eighteenth century, the risk passed from the former to the latter. In any area of modern life to which the scientific mind can gain access the peril is no longer that the past will be uncritically beatified but that it will be contemptuously ignored.

It would be false, however, in trying to salvage something from the past, to claim that it could not be dispensed with. Just as former societies dismissed change as a possibility, so society today can dismiss the past as a major concern. Certainly, in both situations, the unwanted creeps in. No culture that has denied change has been completely successful. Change of some kind, if only decay, has occurred. And no society has yet had the technique or the affluence to deny its past, for the remnants of that past are everywhere, having to be coped with even to the mere effort of their denial.

Certainly it has become a cliché to say that most of the science known today was discovered in the lifetimes of scientists still living. Seminars and workshops are continuously being offered men in their prime years to bring them information about their own disciplines because these fields have been revolutionized since their own college days. It is a fate increasingly common right across the scientific board. It is typical to hear professors lament about an inability to read the current literature in their fields because it is written quantitatively and such terminology was not required learning when they earned their degrees. At biology seminars the participants complain about having to listen to distinguished senior men because, even if they were producers of the recent biological revolution, they are now nothing more than simply history. It is the youthful product of scholarship to whom the middle-aged professionals are most likely to turn so that they may be brought up to date rather than to scholars of their own or a previous generation. This is the mark of the speed with which knowledge has been moving, seeming to accelerate with each decade of the twentieth century.

As a result, the highly contemporary individual sees no hope for models taken from the past. The computer's rise to prominence since 1948 in all research, the use of

quantitative language as a means of expressing even
aesthetic values, the blurring of world values through the
film, radio, and television, the replacement of the printed
word in communication with tape and picture—these
have all been phenomena tending to erase the past and
divert investigators from its study. Even in law libraries
the reports before 1940 are rarely used: The stress is
now put on the most recent case, on the way authority is
going on into the future, and not on how antique a pre-
cedent one has uncovered.

But it is very dangerous to try to shut out past experience from consideration in the present. Whether or not
those who ignore history are condemned to relive it, the
exclusion of a constant concern over actual past experience tends to foster myths about the past. One of the
most persistent is that of the Golden Age. Right now this
is taking the form of a belief that a time and place existed when man did not abuse nature. It is a revival of
the organic school that sees urban man, with his industries and other cash pursuits, as alienated from both his
proper environment and his natural self. Before this contact was broken, man lived in harmony with nature, taking no more than he needed, doing no harm, leaving no
marks upon the landscape, and himself unscarred by the
acts of severing his institutions from nature. As a rejection of technology and the engineering of the environment, it is an idea flourishing today among critics of the
way nature has been and is being processed.

As a warning, a threat, or a dream, there is nothing
wrong in jolting society along these critical patterns.
Considering the number of cheerful optimists, prepared
to justify any demand on nature, any view is valuable
that sees the limits inherent in nature. What is erroneous
is believing the Golden Age bears any relation to fact.
There is, indeed, a serious question as to whether harmony and balance exist anywhere in nature in the sense
that these words are most often used. The natural history
of the world has been one of violent, ceaseless change.
Stability has been a transient episode and most exis-
tences have been stages to something else.

the meaning of balance in nature

Natural relationships express most clearly necessity and convenience, not harmony and balance. When lightning ignites an overage forest, the burned-over area in a temperate climate makes fine deer country. Yet as the forest grows, the zone ceases to be favorable to deer. One form of tree replaces another, moving through transitional stages to the climax, when the forest is once more ripe for the lightning bolt. If this succession means harmony, then fine, except that abrupt climatic changes or earthquakes can throw the whole business into discord. But there is nothing neat and well-ordered about it; it is full of violence, pain, and death; and harmony is rarely used to include events such as these. Yet if harmony refers to a natural balance of this cosmic kind, it is a comprehensible term, however uncommon such a use may be.

What is not so comprehensible is how man can be worked into this kind of harmony. Man, whatever his condition or culture, certainly cannot be any part of it once his numbers pass a trifling absolute figure. For instance, in Ireland there still exist the paths called the Gay Way. They were worn down by the Firbolg, a not especially numerous people who preceded the Gaelic invaders. These conquerors reached Ireland probably around 400 B.C. (certainly not later); they slew the Firbolg and treated the Gay Way accursed, forbidden to any Gael. Thereafter the paths were left untrod; and yet they survived, awing the peasants who took this as part of the proof for the Firbolg's ancient mystic power.

Anyone who has regularly vacationed at a lonely cabin in the forest knows how, after a few seasons, paths get impressed into the earth. If for any reason the cabin is left unvisited for several years, the tracery of the paths remains. A different sort of growth marks where they lie; and one season's light use refurbishes them. Even in the lush tropics an ecologist can often discover where the original plant life, common to the surrounding undisturbed biota, has been replaced by something else that

indicates the need for a transition in order to restore the
prime stage. Such transitions take time; and in human
terms the time needed to remove all evidence of a
human presence can be endless.

This behavior of paths, of course, is not unique to their
human makers. The same is true of all trails made by
creatures of regular habit. Daniel Boone often found himself lost in a maze of trails among the brakes and forests
beyond the Alleghenies. Only a few had been made by
Indians. The rest were the work of deer, woods buffalo,
bear, or even smaller and less gregarious animals. Experienced as Boone was, he often mistook these paths
for human ones. If the forest itself had not been obliterated with its ground put to the plow, those animal trails,
wandering from one water hole to another, would have
remained long after hunters had diminished or killed off
the species who made them. When such a history exists
for the narrow winding forest pathway, no extensive
human demand upon nature can produce a change re-
versible in time units less than geologic ones.

Harmony with nature, therefore, cannot mean for man
any placid, imperceptible passage. It was never true
when his numbers were few; and the revolution in expectations, since the eighteenth century, has made such a
view grossly inappropriate for interpreting man's relations with nature. Man has made himself the commonest
cataclysm in the natural world, the constant destructive
lightning bolt, and here is the problem's crux.

the significance of
"low" current demand

Simply to tour so conservative an area in terms of modern demand as the farming and fishing villages of South
Jersey is to realize man's size. The land uses are frozen
along the survey lines made in the seventeenth century
by the Swedish, Dutch, and English developers. Yet since
that day, the cypress forest that once had its furthest
northern limit there has been reduced to a few forlorn
ragged trees. The creeks and inlets, which were the center of the area's traffic until this century, have silted up
badly so that dredges are continuously chucking up

47

*changing
man's
traditions
about nature*

sludge to keep them open for drainage. The sturgeon, which before 1915 were caught here for shipment to Russia for treatment and reexport to the United States as caviar, have long ceased to be anything except fishermen's curiosities displayed on local wharves as tourist rarities. Truck farms supply canneries and freezers of goods, growing an average of four crops each year and owning or leasing thousands of acres. Though it is a region with all the appearance of a backwater basically carrying on the same ways as when platted in the seventeenth century, this simply is not so. Resource demands are heavy, and their current weight is related directly to the contemporary market demands on the area for truck crops, fishing, and use of waters to receive waste.

Yet it would not be accurate to leave the impression that the demands have only lately reached noticeable proportions. Pollution, for example, stifled the sturgeon and shad catches over half a century ago. For a time, pollution encouraged the oyster and clam populations by warming the water and enriching their food supply; but then various sicknesses, products of pollution, were spread among the shellfish. Steady siltation has been a problem since the cypress, cedar, and pines were felled. It is hard to realize today, standing amid miles of farm country, that this was once fairly thick forest. Only the remnants of miles of cedar "snake" fences and of Swedish houses made of solid cypress blocks 10 feet long stand witness as to why erosion, sedimentation, and silting up of streams have been such long-standing problems.

Probably the present intense cultivation by the large farmers causes far less wear on the land than that of earlier users, because every winter finds the fields closed. The contribution these industrial farms make to perpetuating the difficulties is the consequence of runoff from their field enrichment and pest control programs. It is not siltation that they contribute but massive nutrient pollution. These are tidal waters; and splashing around in that action are all the nutrients applied to the fields at great expense to enrich them as well as the chemicals spread by planes and other kinds of crop dusters as part of the incorporation of agriculture into the modern technology. As such, whatever the other improvements in relation to greater income earned, the demand on resources is in no way diminished from the day when the British raided the area and executed farmers for supplying George Washington's armies. What has occurred since then has been merely an intensification in the character of the demands being made.

Nor is the inability of a region to move over into such intense agricultural use any protection from drastic alteration on that region's resource base. Even when much land is taken out of cultivation or allowed to remain at a level of rather low intensity in terms of what is extracted, it does not mean extensive deterioration cannot be occurring. Southeastern Ohio is such a place. It is far removed, indeed, from either the rich soils or nearby markets of southern New Jersey. It is part of Appalachia; and, as is true of most of Appalachia, farming techniques are not of especially high quality.

But the area is vexed by a problem that good farming might only make worse and that intense extraction of soil values as in southern New Jersey might make unbearable. It is the problem that goes under the folk term of "slickenslides." These are shallow land slides, taking place less than a dozen feet below the surface so that a sliding plane is produced over which the upper soil moves across the lower. Though certain conditions had to be present to make it possible, the deforestation occurring over a century ago and the intervening agriculture have pushed slippage rapidly along by accelerating a wasting of moisture so that clayey materials below the surface can now slide over one another unhindered.

As a problem, it is quite hard to bring to solution. One way out is simply to ignore it, continuing to use the soils in the region as they have been since white settlement entered in the 1780s. This would allow the slipping to go on damaging roads, buildings, or fields that could then either be allowed to stay in such deteriorated state or else restored. In the economic poverty in the area this remains the probable course of action.

Perhaps it is not the worst alternative available, either. An exactly contrary proposal would intervene with large engineering works meant to protect highways and other substantial installations by first stripping away all these shifting earths until the solid levels were revealed and then building thereon with firm foundations. Aside from its utility being limited to just a few situations, and putting aside the required investment in earth-moving, it takes no nature lover to see that this is the engineering of desperation.

What is needed in southeastern Ohio is a restoration of the original moisture conditions in the soil. This means a rapid elimination of the subsistence agriculture and a heavy investment in reforestation, at least where slippage is worst, even if it means directing highways around these zones and their return to relative wilderness. The same restoration of earlier conditions is needed in the streams and inlets of southern New Jersey. What are not needed are the big engineering schemes that call for periodic drainage of streams, the digging out of sediment, and the attempts to fix the banks with rock. Aside from the massive damage to life forms, it is a fiscally expensive process that begins showing its failure almost before the workmen can move away their tools.

What also must come are the retirement of the remaining subsistence farms, the avoidance of too "clean" a field program so that fences, gullies, and creeks remain brushy, the building of a drainage system that will filter chemically laden runoff water, the closing of fields in winter, and a close control so waste is not allowed to wash away into the already overburdened creeks. They are small measures, not very costly compared to some of the engineering schemes, but they can come closer to solving the problem and leaving the areas still available for substantial human use. Such places cannot be left to slow deterioration because they seem unchanging backwaters in comparison with the urban centers. There are no longer any isolated sweet Auburns; and it is blindness to pretend differently.

*preservation as
an act of destruction*

Everything man touches in nature is altered by that contact, often in such a way that makes the human action seem like a multiplier of effects exceeding the most extreme predictions. Nor are motives any protection against harms wrought. Making deserts bloom is a common human aspiration that seems as if it must be a basically good idea, either for the human economy or its environment. Yet not all the results are benefits for either the economy or the ecology.

First of all, making the desert bloom is to end its existence as a desert. All the life forms that have adjusted to arid conditions are now reduced or obliterated so that a highly artificial situation is created. The desert with water added becomes a hothouse for exotics. Like the hothouse, it is subject to deterioration, requires continuous maintenance, is highly unstable, and lasts only as long as there is a human society capable of keeping it going. Should any weakening occur in that capacity, the whole irrigation culture is thrown into crisis and its transiency exposed. Nor, if it should collapse, is there any guaranty the previous desert life forms will return, for the intervening irrigation may have terminated them.

That is only a part of the chancy results, and to an economist it is not likely to have major significance, especially in an economy like the United States where only a violent wrench would ensue if all irrigation had to be stopped. Even if all the American Southwest were lost to desolation, the national economy would survive, perhaps even being vivified by the need to relocate so much activity. Economically, what is of immediate consequence from irrigation, unless it is pumped from below ground, is that other regions become mere water sources. Their future is exchanged for an investment thrust to social and economic programs pushing for settlement in places naturally less desirable, if not downright catastrophically unsuited for anything except a very light human use.

Furthermore, when land is irrigated by relatively pure water, it washes out mineral content from the soil. Every irrigation project is also a drainage project, so these mineral salts are washed into waters downstream. In fact, when heavy mineralization is to be cleaned out of soil, it is done by sluicing water over the fields, flushing it away, and thereby leaching out all salts. Conversely, when it is the water that is high in minerals while the soil is low, irrigation builds up mineral deposits until the soil cannot grow crops. In both instances the process is intensified by evaporation and absorption.

Nor is the cure some vast scheme for removing all salts so they can be isolated somewhere. Where clay lies below ground, these salts act as electrolytic binding agents. When they are gone, the result will be "quick clay," a gooey mass that is most unstable and over which the whole surface will move at the least tremor. There are sites naturally possessing this phenomenon, such as Anchorage, Alaska; and for them the proposals are not to expand such deposits, but to find some way to bind them—such as forcing in salts. Making the desert bloom is not, therefore, a business without considerable expenses on the side.

In nature there exists a degree of interrelatedness hard for man to either comprehend or handle. Nothing seems to be isolated. Neutrality is unknown. Of course, it is the human view that sees elements in nature competing with or complementing each other. Yet when some soils cannot be dried out without risk of slickenslide, and other soils cannot be moistened without the peril of making quick clay, it is evident even at the level of nonliving resources that delicate connections exist which it is dangerous in the extreme to ignore.

In these instances it is not the extent of the human demand that matter. In the case of the slickenslides of southeastern Ohio the cause is fairly minimal in terms of normal human demand, while for the risk of making quick clay such a result would be the consequence of massive investments in water transfer and an unprecedented demand upon water and soil resources. Still, whatever the comparative size of the human investment or expectation producing the harm, it is the scope of the damage that has primary importance. The vaster the scheme that ignores the interconnectedness of geologic conditions, the greater the consequences upon the conditions. The balance, after all, is often so fragile that, as at Denver recently, the injection of waste water through a shaft into deep strata can trigger almost continuous earth tremors. Only stopping of the forced pumpage halted the quakes. Given a relationship such as this, even geology becomes a field of potentially unstable, shiftable balances.

Yet it is in the living environment that the delicacy of balance is far more evident. One example is fishing in the Great Lakes. Although rich in commercial catches down to the 1950s, the fish life there was profoundly upset by the opening of the sea-going canals and the rising pollution. For a time it appeared that one of the species introduced as a result of the sea-going canals, the coho salmon, would replace for commercial purposes many of the destroyed native species. State hatcheries acted to speed up their development, and it seemed as if a healthy substitute had been found. It has been called "the fish management achievement of the century." Not only did they prove popular with recreational fishermen, but a commercial coho industry also was born, so that between them a substantial income was brought to areas of the Great Lakes, possibly even exceeding that which had been lost through the diminution of native fish species. It seemed as if a story with a sad beginning was about to have a happy and relatively easy ending.

However, whatever the ultimate outcome, enough has now transpired to show it cannot be easy. The future of the entire program has been menaced by the effect of DDT, the most popular of the chlorinated hydrocarbon pesticides, on the coho and, as an indirect possibility, on those eating the coho. It has settled on the land and from there been washed into the lakes. Unfortunately, the "life" of this and related pesticides is hard to determine, with the further problem that some break down into more toxic forms, combine with other elements to potentiate a more lethal effect, or produce a more serious consequence on other species than on those for which death was originally intended. The consequence is often insidious, for the chemicals become unevenly stored in the tissues of fish living in water thus polluted, so that harm is not immediately observed. The fish reproductive process is particularly vulnerable and in 1968 seemed to be responsible for a "die-off" of many coho fingerlings in state hatcheries. In the long run coho numbers will probably be reduced and the survivors may be inedible.

Man, whatever his chemical prowess, is also a vulnerable creature. The Federal Food and Drug Administration has set, somewhat arbitrarily, five parts per million (though formerly 3.5 ppm) of DDT in coho, whereas the measurement by 1969 had reached up to 22 parts per million and was rising. As it is, the health agencies urge that no one eat the belly flesh of the coho and use of DDT around lakes Superior and Michigan was prohibited as of June, 1969. Unfortunately, even when all use of "hard" pesticides stops, their strength will take over two decades to disappear.

the limits the past puts on the present

The natural environment of man, whether considered geologically or biologically, is composed of intimate relationships that are disturbed by the least action of man, sometime even irreversibly so. Because of this, there is no way man can erase the past and begin again with a fresh start. The acts of men in previous ages set the limits on much of man's course in the modern or future world. Millennia of abuse have sharply reduced available human resource options. Furthermore, what can be done to stop the steady destruction must be carried on in terms of restoring the natural conditions so persistently assaulted for so long a time. As Paul Goodman said, in speaking of cultural history, "We are not only free organisms but parts of mankind that has historically made itself with great inspirations and terrible conflicts. We cannot slough off that accumulation, however burdensome, without becoming trivial and therefore servile." In no area of human experience is this more true than in man's relationship to nature.

Past, present, and future are very close, indeed, so far

as man's relationship with his environment is concerned. What has been done affects what is being done; and this, in turn, determines the future. Virgin territory, unaffected by human use, grows more scarce continuously. It truly does not exist at all in the sense of total effect, for the universal spread of pesticides and air pollution in the past generation prevents such pockets from surviving. What most nearly approaches Shangri-La, those stretches of land rarely penetrated by man's own physical presence, is being increasingly considered for that fact alone as natural resources calling for preservation. As the world population increases, even though the tendency seems to be to concentrate upon less and less ground, the growing demands on the environment put ever larger tracts under the dire threat of permanent change. If any of these relatively unexploited zones are to survive over the next three generations, the plans to save them must be made immediately. Otherwise, within that rather brief time period, even the most remote parts of the Congo and Amazon valleys will have been processed into the urban-industrial civilization.

What must not be forgotten is that this processing of the environment is accelerating. If man is 1¾ million years old, his numbers and technology did not allow him to make a permanent impress upon nature until less than fifteen thousand years ago. He had to domesticate plants and animals, break the soil for planting, fell trees, divert water, and adapt to village life in order to make lasting changes in nature. The pace, however much proof exists for its demands over many millennia, has recently picked up markedly. Think for a moment of how much of the world was in a natural state in the eighteenth century. What was not unpeopled was but lightly touched by its inhabitants. The eighteenth century was the last moment of time, when so much of nature would be untouched by human activity.

But in the eighteenth century the whole world was caught up in the kind of escalation of human demand upon its environment that has produced a universal crisis. In terms of resource demands primitive peoples increasingly ceased to be technically simple. Far more advanced tools were given them and, often, they were tied into world markets at the same time, with effects upon resources every bit as profound as what the inventors of that more advanced technology could themselves have wrought. As early as the mid-seventeenth century, the Huron Indians, who had been in contact with French fur traders since 1550, had extirpated the beaver in their hunting territories. It was to be that animal's sad fate with one tribe after another. Later the Bannock and northern Shoshone, who before 1800 had lacked horses for hunting, had by 1840 exterminated the buffalo in the Great Basin and were forced to the eastern slopes of the Rockies for further kills.

*the danger of relying
entirely on the future*

Steadily, without slack or cessation, this escalation has intensified over the time interval, so very brief in natural terms, since the eighteenth century. Though all man's history is a prelude and a preparation, the technology and economics flourishing ever more abundantly since the eighteenth century are without precedence in the ability they have revealed in shrinking first the world and then the universe beyond it. The very young, in truth, begin to act as if this planet earth could be abandoned and another existence pursued elsewhere. There either the earthly mistakes would not be made or else would take so long to be fatal for the colonies upon those dead stars that the pioneers could be as cavalier as their own ancestors were throughout earth's history.

It is a cruel, if bewitching, fantasy, rather like a man sacrificing an unbaptized infant at a Black Mass in order to gain a few years' longevity. First of all, every scrap of investment for space travel and settlement must be carved out of earth's resources. No one should overlook the cost to earth's resources of the kinds of settlements, or even stations, so glibly commended for the moon, Mars, or some more remote post—unless, of course, this planet is to be treated like the wrecked vessel from which the Swiss Family Robinson extracted the means for life in a new land.

Yet that, too, is a fraudulent image. The wilderness for the Robinsons was a genial one, rich in resources, waiting only for the toil of that diligent family to respond with extravagent production. By the end of the novel it has been converted to a subtropical but thoroughly subdued suburb of Zurich. What makes their experience incompatible with that of space travelers is that the colonists on other planets must from the first, and thereafter forever, have an environment completely artificial and exotic to the planet where they are landed. The wilderness was a natural milieu for the Robinsons. This cannot be true for earth colonists on other planets. What will have to be done at the outset on another planet is to set up conditions the Robinsons took for granted; and that will have to be done out of the resources of the planet from which the colonists have come.

The only reason to mention any of this is to reveal how easily persons are prepared to draw lavishly upon earth's resources in order to build unstable artificial environments on other planets. This represents sophistication and futuristic thinking, whereas concern for maintaining a viable balance between human demand and its earthly home is somehow neither for these people. Perhaps some of the plans for sustaining the needed artificial conditions for human life on the moon may have to be put to creating artificial regimes for a similar purpose upon a polluted earth. Such a future development, indeed, would be an ironic proof of the interconnectedness of all knowledge, most particularly for those who pushed forward such knowledge in the hope earth's problems could be carelessly put aside or left behind.

the problem of
nature's interrelatedness

The one inescapable fact in nature is that everything interrelates. Because man is a creature dependent on his environment, he is a part of nature, with his every desire having to be taken from it. The more vaunting the schemes of human reason, the nearer man comes to his last choice: to assume the responsibility for his environment or allow matters to go skittering on to catastrophe.

Past events, present actions, future aspirations, cannot be treated in isolation from each other. No part of the world is a refuge from the urban-industrial civilization. Water, clay, rock, nitrogen, oxygen, and other nonliving substances interconnect in subtle ways it can be perilous to disturb. Many of these either compose the living organism or are vital to its survival. It would be a poor business, indeed, to sacrifice some essential element to life for some cash profit. The myth of King Midas would have been reenacted in that event on a cosmic scale.

However, it is in the relations living things have to each other that the most essential intimacy prevails. Living entities form food chains, leading from predator to predator, which compose the connections called ecosystems. These chains, when broken by having a link knocked out, are often able to repair themselves through substitution or by closing up. If the link destroyed were more important or if several links were simultaneously removed, then the ecosystem might collapse and its survivors find a place elsewhere. After all, ecosystems themselves are not isolates and, therefore, have crossover points for refugees from a destroyed neighboring ecosystem. It is this almost magical resiliency that has permitted life to survive on a planet beset throughout its history with one catastrophe after another. Without it, the problem would long since have ceased to present itself.

Yet this resiliency ought not to be too freely relied on, particularly when the need for it is being compressed into ever shorter time spans. Man himself is the most omnivorous of species. Once the full range of man's food is listed, it can be seen most clearly that he eats about anything; and that for him the term "edible" is very expandable. But this sort of wide choice is not true for other species; and the smaller and more ephemeral they are, the fewer their feeding options. Because these last are themselves food for so many others, their having insoluble feeding problems causes repercussions of far greater consequence than would ensue if, say, the great rhino should become extinct.

It is the relationships themselves that are vital rather than any single element within them. What has to be viewed with alarm is not the loss of any one species but what this loss means to the ecosystem of which it is a part. Too often in the past, whenever some single species has been threatened, the argument has been about its individual importance. After the argument has been lost by those pleading to preserve the endangered species (as usually it has been) and after nature has closed over the absent one without a seeming ripple, those who have taken the opposite position have appeared justified by the lack of dramatic results. Who today misses the passenger pigeon? Never having known this bird, subsequent generations can scarcely claim to miss it.

Truthfully, there are many species now under threat of elimination whom man's economy would not miss and for whose loss nature could come to fairly quick accommodation. Some of them, like the Key deer, are regional peculiarities, marginal survivors in their own habitat, likely involved in an unstable adjustment in any case. Such species as these may be valuable to man for finding how survival is possible outside the place and time most congenial to the surviving creature; but apart from this, they could slip away unnoticed by men, other than scholars, and with a smooth transition in nature following their demise. However, what is compounding the slight single loss to nature in the case of each extinguished species is the great variety lost or threatened in the past century. What one by one might be treated as a small deduction from a rich total has become, once again by operation of urban-industrial civilization, a sum of potentially heavy loss, indeed.

The important blows are the ones to an entire ecosystem or to the whole of the ecology rather than to one or more species. It is the difference between eliminating one type of butterfly or all butterflies, one kind of songbird or all birds, one sort of fish or all aquatic life. In man's own personal life he prefers a medication that knocks out bacteria dangerous to him rather than a regimen that would give him the general health to overcome these bacteria. This is so even though it risks the destruction of beneficial bacteria absolutely essential to human life, or lethal allergic reactions, or loss of any chance at inherited immunities. However pleasant it may be to never contract smallpox, measles, whooping cough, diphtheria, mumps, or scarlet fever, modern man after several generations of this will be completely dependent upon his artificial protectors. A political break in the present organization of affairs, which would make impossible the carrying on of the present immunization programs, could precipitate disastrous epidemics. Yet this is the risk that has been undertaken and that remains the preferred solution. Assuredly, if man adopts such a regime for his own body, he will tend to do no less for the totality of nature.

Such an approach, however, requires a wide scope of knowledge, itself approaching a total product. The more completely natural means of balance are departed from or the better artificial means work in postponing natural phenomena, the greater the pressure needed from the natural phenomena to overcome the artificial constraints on them and the greater the investment needed to keep up the constraint. Artificial devices become fragile with age; and catastrophe, should the constraints collapse under the high pressure of natural phenomena, must result. It is this burden man undertakes when he decides to replace natural behavioral patterns with a plan more suited in his eyes to human economic benefit. In such a situation what must be viewed with increasing apprehension is not any matter of single harm in nature, but rather the danger to all life itself. There is nothing wrong in struggling to preserve a single species or locale from destruction as long as such individual efforts are coordinated and as long as no effort is made to avoid seeing that the danger comes from man himself in what he demands from nature.

the future's difference
from the past in nature

It is the confrontation man has provoked with his environment, now so clearly in its acute stage, that is different than anything known in the past. Previous ages, by what they did, contributed to the present situation; and, through the way they formed current cultural outlook, they are still contributing. But these previous people did not have the crisis on the scale on which it presently stands. Their experience, when they faced anything comparable, is rather gloomy. Soil exhaustion for the Mayan, soil mineralization for the Indies and the Tigris-Euphrates civilizations, seems to have meant disastrous consequences, just about terminal for complex economic forms in those areas.

These ancient economies lacked the variety of income sources today available, and, of course, they had nothing like the present technology which, though contributing to intensifying the problem, is also capable of a reversal that would make a favorable resolution possible. Though the ecology of the world is threatened by human demand on an unprecedented scale, there is available, partly from what has been learned out of the very acts of destruction themselves, a great deal that has application to conserving as well as using up the life within man's environment. More important even than this, perhaps, is the fact that the danger is known, its sources identified, its solutions fairly well sketched out. These facts alone make a unique difference. Previous cultures may have had vague, poetic, religious, or mystical opinion as to the importance of protecting nature or of maintaining balance among all living things. But aside from their generality, such views had little in them to make them effective for any purpose other than engendering guilt among the few sensitive abusers of nature.

Today, however, the knowledge is not of the kind intuited by some poet. It is, instead, measurable, as assessible to the scientific community as any branch of knowledge for which similar techniques are usable. True, without scientific proof or technical instruments the mystics saw that these balances were vital to continued existence for man and the other life-form and life-sustaining substances so needed by him, despite his preoccupation with establishing human autonomy in relation to them. But science has proven that man's autonomy is a dream, and quite an unwholesome one when he seeks to act it out. For the foreseeable future he will continue to be connected with both other living organisms and with the *changing man's traditions about nature* substances necessary to sustain life, for man is very far from being a creature of pure mind.

Humanity needs these other forms and substances because, without their being present in a considerable amount, he cannot exist in any number or in much comfort; and if they do not subsist at all, then neither does he. Briefly, he will have made himself lord of a charnel house and, after that, nothing at all—unless, once more, he takes his place among the lesser angels. It would be a most condemning commentary upon the ultimate worth of human reason, which has been man's claim for a special place above all other forms of life. To have the ability reason gives man to stand aside from the rush of events so as objectively to appraise them and to do no more with it than connive in furthering clearly seen terminal catastrophe is to pass the most severe judgment possible on all the works of man. If human history finally stands for no more than this, there will be no final difference between those who observed it and those who simply ignored the whole business, because both will have suffered the same fate. In terms of law and history, man would have tried himself and been found wanting. In the terms of nature, which has no such references to value judgments, the course of life would have come to the end. Whether this comes to pass depends on the extent to which urban-industrial civilization is diverted from purely processing the environment to preserving the life-sustaining elements.

REFERENCES

The American Environment: Readings in the History of Conservation, Roderick Nash, ed., Reading, Mass.: Addison-Wesley, 1968.

Raymond F. Dasmann, *Environmental Conservation,* 2nd ed., New York: 1968.

René Dubos, *Mirage of Health: Utopias, Progress and Biological Change,* Garden City, N.Y.: Anchor Books, 1961.

Aldo Leopold, *A Sand County Almanac and Sketches*

Here and There, New York: Oxford University Press, 1968.

Russell Lord, *The Care of the Earth, A History of Husbandry,* New York: Mentor Books, 1963.

Gene Marine, *America the Raped: The Engineering Mentality and the Destruction of a Continent,* New York: Simon and Schuster, 1969.

Jaro Mayda, *Environment and Resources: From Conservation to Ecomanagement,* San Juan: University of Puerto Rico Law School, 1968.

Gerard Piel, *Science in the Cause of Man,* 2nd ed., New York: Vintage Books, 1964.

Sir George Thomson, *The Foreseeable Future,* 2nd ed., New York: Viking Press, 1960.

Kenneth E. F. Watt, *Ecology and Resource Management: A Quantitative Approach,* New York: McGraw-Hill, 1968.

4

how
free
is nature
to man?

*the interrelatedness of
costs from resource use*

One of the commonest opinions held inter-
prets nature as a free source of supply for
whatever human purposes man can conceive. The only costs to be calculated, in
pursuing this view, are those pertaining to
the human activity alone. Thus the costs for
fishing are summarized in the money it
takes to equip a fleet, pay the fishermen,
and process the catch for market. No
thought is given to the larger charge on the
interrelated life systems of which every marine species is a part. The fish, once they
are taken, are treated as if they were a
nonliving resource. But the living and self-
renewing resources are not of this sort;
and to massively exploit them is both to
subject them to heavy charges and to discount them rapidly in time.

It is the tradition to use whatever lies
naturally at hand to assist some particular
enterprise and to treat this natural presence as a free gift. The disposal of trash
increasingly marks the progress of the affluent society. Industrial waste, detergent
foam, municipal sewage, agricultural runoff, the funds of an economy prosperous
and adept enough both to have throwaways
and to prosper from their use, all comprise

63

the stuff of a human demand on nature. They are burned, which scatters them as air pollution; flushed, which creates the problems of siltation and water pollution; or turned under, thereby polluting the soil. The role of nature is as a receptor, provided free of cost for a booming urban-industrial economy. The leading drawback for the future is simply the fact that nature cannot serve either as a garbage dump or as a source of economic well-being, free of cost.

Of course, it is possible to interconnect certain human demands so that one acts as an offset to the other. The strip-mining industry has left gaping holes, tearing open the land and exposing it to an interaction with the elements that has contributed mightily to acid water pollution, erosion, and the general conferring of desert conditions on large areas. Once the streams are dug out, not even the payrolls of the strip miners are left—and, because modern technique requires a few workmen in such operations, they are scant payrolls at their best. The practice has too often been to leave the landscape as a blasted heath.

The reason restoration has not been popular is the very difficulty in doing more than rounding off the rougher edges, leaving behind water-filled depressions and soil incapable of sustaining plant life. Pennsylvania has since 1943 maintained the oldest restoration program. It has not been the success the original hopes held for it, partly because of a sheer lack of prosthetic material to use for rebuilding the dug-out ground and as an insulator against acid. This has produced a recommendation of hauling solid waste by rail (in other states a waste pipeline is projected), so that the compacted solid waste can be used as fill and as insulator. Ideally, such country can by these means be brought back more nearly to its original conditions.

In a manner such as this, one problem can be used to solve another where urban-industrial areas adjoin a region of abandoned strip mines and where hopes of a return from such territories in the guise of recreation dollars are also maintained. Pennsylvania meets both of these tests. In addition the slag heaps that clogged so many valleys there, poisoning streams and fouling the air, are being used to form a cementlike filler for burning shaft mines that will both extinguish the fires and fill up the workings to prevent settling. Anyone familiar with Pennsylvania, however, knows how little restoration has occurred, relative to the total need, and to what extent the cities there are still choking in their own output of waste.

Still, this is a beginning along a line of reciprocal problem-solving. What pushes these programs along, however, is lack of economic alternatives. There is little land located near big cities for the traditional burial dump. The scavengers are having to go ever greater distances in order to dispose of waste; and unless a pipeline can chuck the stuff off the continental shelf, rail haulage to the coal country in the mountains of the mid-Atlantic states will be competitive. This is buttressed by the need to restore these mountains for masses of city dwellers hungry for the recreation. They are prepared to pump money into these exhausted areas in an amount that every decade comes closer to surpassing whatever the coal industry brought them.

To explore northeastern Pennsylvania, for example, is to see that such enterprises as lumbering, agriculture, and mining took far more out of the local economy than they ever put back in; and recreation, joined with light industry in the towns, is the only business that can restore the balance. Commercial forestry is not practicable, as shown by the inability of the Forest Service to maintain a full cutting program in this district. Yet those forests have served as excellent soil and water retainers and as a place where a person from the city can go to play with nature. The use of this area by the city masses is scarcely in its opening stages; and the problem in the future is not going to be how recreation can share the region with other uses, but rather how all the recreation uses can be accommodated without overwhelming what is there. The risk is the belief recreation can earn back everything the region had skinned off it in the past by its previous and successive exploiters: lumbering, agriculture, and mining.

In the course of events, that will be the tendency; and it will be so because nature in this area was treated by these earlier businesses as if it were a free good, whereas all along it was an integral part of the profit-and-loss picture. Only, while lumbering, agriculture, and mining were allowed to carry off the profit and leave the loss behind, the pressure upon the recreation enterprise will be to recoup all the past losses from it; and if this is permitted to push on unchecked, the ultimate outcome will not be recoupment but a larger and perhaps finally catastrophic loss. Whatever the enterprise that rests on nature, there are limits to what the resources can bear to support; and to surpass those limits is to connect an apparent surplus to a real loss.

the inability of
nature to be a free good

This should make clear that nature, once drawn into the human economy, can be treated neither as something valueless nor as a free good in the economy. Of course, accountants for processing enterprises have assigned book values to their companies' property, so that for tax, borrowing, and capital purposes the forests, minerals, or other objects of exploitation have regularly been assigned some worth, although the amount has been due to legal or market peculiarities rather than to any value to be assigned from natural function. Most valuable natural uses have never been assigned a book value by business executives. Water in wells, a receiving body for waste, the air either as a life need or as a receiver of effluent, have been a value only as a subsumed part of the enterprise using them. When the demand on nature's resources has been most gross, this subsumed worth acts to lower drastically the value of an entire area affected by the dominant activity. Entire tracts, for example, have had their income producibility destroyed by some neighboring enterprise that has blithely subsumed within itself some part of nature as a free gift.

Free, nature is not, however. It cannot even be used for the piling up of the debris of modern civilization without a cost calculation of what is being lost or gained and what positive and negative values other actions might have as alternative forms of behavior. In the ancient past, householders trod their castoffs underfoot or cast them over the city wall. The waste disposal problem has been inherent in city living from Jericho to Manhattan; and yet, by a geometric expansion of waste, urban-industrial civilization has altered the scope of what must be dealt with.

The solutions, instead, must be on the grand scale of the problem as newly redefined by modern industry. Some proposals call for extruding pipe to the edge of the North American continental shelf to dispose of solvent wastes. Others would pulverize solids into a slurry for dumping into the sea. Some would use all that was flammable to provide the power for water desalination plants, as in the one at Hong Kong fueled by garbage. There is proposed a thirty-year plan in the Ruhr for piling waste upon the ground, shaping it with dozers, planting trees, and ultimately enjoying a hilly, wooded recreational area on what originally had been a flat. The Ruhr plan shares with all the others the same feature: the necessity for grandiosity. Suddenly what had been regarded as trivial, the concern of derelicts raking in the haze of a burning dump and of a few political hacks in the sanitation department, holds out the prospect of massive expenditures.

The traditional style was never a free one and the cost of it is mounting frightfully. André Malraux has said that man introduces to nature the experience of real death, that before man works his metamorphosis, the only death nature knows is the constant renewal of life. But man incorporates nature into his transient structures; and for the first time a death is produced that leaves behind it no prospect of renewal. Eternity has been exchanged for mortality by converting nature into a resource of the human economy.

the meaning of
depreciation for nature

Economists insist that the concept of depreciation ought to apply only to man-made objects. It is inherent in the fact that every human creation perishes. Maintenance can delay this event, but even the act of delaying gives full recognition to the inevitability of depreciation in all human constructs. Any appreciation in value is not inherent in the thing itself but in externalities that make valuable works of art or ancient buildings, even after their delicate senescent condition has lost all function for them except simply to continue existing. This process of depreciation is a factor that must be included in any embrasive economic equation.

Yet economists tell us depreciation does not inure in the renewable resources that man uses. Streams continue to flow, soil to rebuild itself, grass to reseed itself, wildlife to be born, even as man draws upon them. Only the stock resources are held to be subject to depreciation, for as man takes from them he reduces the overall supply permanently. It has been found, unfortunately, that such stock resources have been far commoner than was once imagined.

Water below ground can be in nonreplenishable layers so that pumping it is mining it. Perennial grasses, when overgrazed, can cease to reseed themselves and become extinct. Forests, seeming to flourish, are actually at a sere state to which a return will not be possible due to altered conditions incapable of permitting a forest to restart itself. Forms of wildlife, abundant in numbers, may yet be relics of a past age, without capacity for regeneration once a very fragile balance has been upset.

Each of these, although appearing to be self-renewing, is in actuality a stock resource. Indeed, they are even more destructible than ores since these exist in varying degrees of richness in the earth, enabling man to shift from pure to adulterated sources as he successively exhausts them. This is not true for the exhaustible, although apparently self-renewing, resources. When they are gone, the shifting has to be to species only somewhat less vulnerable or, in the case of water, to irreclaimable desert; and depreciation has repeatedly proven to be rapid.

Still, in the case of those resources possessing sufficient support in surrounding conditions to be truly self-renewing, it is said that the concept of depreciation is not applicable except where human intervention has built the resource beyond the point of self-sustenance. Soil can be built, for example, to an artificial level far above its natural conditions; but this surplus is subject to depreciation and, once human support is withdrawn, a reversion to a lower condition ensues. But in the natural soil itself depreciation is said not to occur because the soil is engaged in constant renewal, which replaces what is taken from it. For nature at its self-renewing best, exhaustion is not possible, for everything taken away is promptly replaced.

However, once nature is drawn into the human economy, it acquires characteristics similar to human products. Imitation, repetition, simulation, are the only means available to man to repeat his creations once his efforts fail to maintain them against the depreciating force of inexorable decay. Modern urban-industrial economics, in fact, seeks to work in favor of depreciation. The reason it chokes in its own waste with an intensity never before known is because it is quite uninterested in an original long-term manufacture. Neighborhoods are modeled on automobiles, something to be traded up or down socially and discarded every generation. The new is sought, the old discarded without effort at salvage, and on this attitude prosperity is kept up. The passing moment is what is stressed in human affairs; and it can scarcely fail to shape attitudes to natural elements as well.

Many, indeed, are perturbed that nature can no longer renew itself in many areas without human intervention. Forestry experts claim that it is a serious matter that in the new tree growth in much of the eastern United States no selective cutting is being done. In western Massachusetts only 13 percent of the original owners still hold the land, while the rest has passed to city dwellers who hold it for recreational purposes. For them a tree is a tree, regardless of species, so long as it is green, casts a shade, and rustles in the evening wind. Anyhow, their holdings are too small to economically keep up brush clearance, cutting, or planting unless they could be organized into forest districts to which they would pay a specific charge for supplying these services. Silviculturists accuse these hapless exurbanites with creating a "biological desert." It is a harsh indictment, considering that their "junk" trees are helping hold soil to the hills, keep streams clear, retain water in the highlands, and stop the sort of skinning the natives engaged in for cordwood, small sawmills, and pulp. Even so, however, if the eastern American forest is to make a major return, massive human effort is required; and the job will be a far more complex one than that of cutting it down in the first place.

So long as the human economy coasts along the surface of its environment, the renewing resources will replenish whatever is taken from them. But once this sort of activity ceases and the use turns intense, the natural resources are more and more worked into the human economy until, ultimately, they acquire its attributes. The idea of depreciation, in the sense of destroying the renewing capacity, covers both the artificial and the natural parts of the integrated human economy; and man has acquired the responsibility both for what he made and for what he took into his economy. What had appeared to be free had abruptly altered into a very expensive component which could be no more neglected than any other part of the economic mechanism if that mechanism were not rapidly to fray and fall apart.

the real expenses in resource use

After all, what in humid climates has seemed freer than water? Forgetting the worth it has in arid lands, water in most of the northern hemisphere has been treated as a free gift. Nevertheless, again forgetting the falsely low prices political regimes have set upon water, water in the late twentieth century is a heavy expense for urban-industrial society. Fresh water taken from natural surface sources and delivered by gravitational flow, without filtration and treated only with chlorination, costs over 15 cents per thousand gallons. When this water has to be pumped from deep wells or accumulated in reservoirs, demineralized, filtered, aerated, or delivered by energy-pumping, the cost rises materially. When some raw water suppliers in east Texas are paid on anciently frozen rates as low as ¾ of *one* cent per thousand gallons, it is evident that costs are not being met but rather that something of very great value is still being given away at some entity's expense.

In the past the loss was made up out of nature's so-called free gifts. But now it is the public treasury that is expected to supply the deficiency. There is nothing free about water; and any businessman who has had to locate an enterprise in relation to a large, steady, or pure supply of water can testify amply to that effect.

Robert Frost, no economist assuredly, has still contrived a humorous "editorial" about the result of passing on such losses, basing it on an inscription found at Ctesiphon, a ruined Roman city not far from Babylon.

. . .

THE ART OF LIFE IS PASSING LOSSES ON.
The city saying it was Ctesiphon,
Which may a little while by war and trade
Have kept from being caught with the decayed,
Infirm, worn-out, and broken on its hands;
But judging by what little of it stands,
Not even the ingenuities of debt
Could save it from its losses being met.
Sand has been thrusting in the square of door
Across the tessellation of the floor,
And only rests, a serpent on its chin,
Content with contemplating, taking in,
Till it can muster breath inside a hall
*To rear against the inscription on the wall.**

The humor, of course, is in the poem and not in the situation. Yet the point is made, even so, that such losses are not to be passed on except as an illusion.

Nevertheless, it is a stubborn illusion that is expiring reluctantly. At a time when no part of nature on this planet is unaffected in some way by urban-industrial so-

* Robert Frost, "The Ingenuities of Debt," *The Poetry of Robert Frost,* Edward Connery Lathem, ed., New York, Holt, Rinehart and Winston, 1969. Reprinted by permission of the publisher.

ciety and when there is an ever closer integration of nature into that economy, people still think of serving out
free goods from nature: whales and fish at sea, virgin
forests, wild grass for grazing herds, water for receiving
waste, and the air itself as the largest sewer of all. Yet
even as the search goes on, the substance of the illusion
continues shrinking.

Whales are rarely to be sighted near the continental
coastline, certainly not in numbers for commercial hunting; and so scarce are they becoming for the factory
fleets, capable of converting leviathan to cat food in a
few hours, that gamblers are betting certain whale species will be extinct by 1980. Diplomats are urged to talk
about fish protection zones, closely policed and with
catch limits set by international convention; but the poor
success of such agreements to guard whales, seals, and
other sea mammals has done little but effectively reserve
their exploitation to fewer than half a dozen great powers.

The marine states quarreling over fish are like graziers
holding licenses in the public lands for their herds and
flocks who regard the grasslands as meant by nature for
these and not to be shared with wild grass eaters like
moose and elk or with recreationists. Only the Defense
Department with its need of high pastures for biological
and gas experimentation has been able to dislodge them
with a higher claim to the public domain. For any other
purposes the herders have been pretty much able to take
the same attitude they held toward the nesters: illegiti-
mate interlopers seeking something from nature which
was not theirs, whatever statutes, regulations, or court
orders may say.

choices in ocean
resource development

In case of ocean as for other resources, there do exist
men of larger, if no more altruistic, vision. The Maltese
Resolution of 1967 sees all states of the world, regardless of power or proximity to the sea, as equally entitled
to share in all marine resources. In order to guarantee

this equality the deep ocean should be put under the jurisdiction of an agency of the United Nations. Indeed, the proposal would vest in the United Nations the attributes of ownership. For granting franchises, royalties could be charged, calculated on the value of what would be taken, and under no circumstances would any absolute dominion be sold in perpetuity. Part of these monies, coming from such enterprises as oil and gas wells, machines for picking metallic ores off the ocean floor, mines beneath the sea bed, fishing, gathering marine flora, using the ocean for a settling basin, or any use other than navigation, would be employed to give the United Nations independent financing. The remainder would be invested in developing basic structures in countries not sufficiently integrated into the world urban-industrial economy. It is not concerned primarily with the ultimate condition of the ocean; but with so many beneficiaries, having as protracted a need for income from this source for the indefinite future, one of the indirect benefits ought to be some protection of the planet's marine resources.

Yet, at the moment, the likely future development must apparently come closer to marine exhaustion before an effective international administration can be set up to prevent their destruction. Current trends indicate the oceans will probably be treated by the nations the way private landowners divide up the rights in nonnavigable lakes. This would cut up the oceans in pie-shaped chunks for each seaside state to control for its domestic purposes, perhaps vaguely limited by some internationally adopted rules. If this is done, it does not bode well for the marine resources. Sea creatures are many of them highly mobile, so that even if one of the states is a cautious exploiter of its assigned share, they will suffer from the depreciations of the ruthless takers. At the last, the standards will be set through force of economic pressure by the most exploitative of the states until the biologic break occurs. By then, unfortunately, given the scale of everything connected with the ocean, the task of restoration has every prospect of being beyond the scope of man's ability to handle it. In such a crisis, laments will have the hollow ring of any debtor's cries. Un-

74

man and his environment: law

fortunately, the survival and new beginning available to the private debtor through bankruptcy will not be present when the ocean's resources have been drawn down to near zero.

costs in public expenditures on resources

Of course perhaps all this is laboring a point. Perhaps there has been an unconscious realization by man that nothing is free from nature if he wants it in substantive, regular, and controllable quantities. After all, water resources, when demanding those characteristics, have been assigned large portions of various economies in order to make water so available. Occasionally a few other resources have received similar treatment, such as the German forest since the eighteenth century, or soil in Japan, or game on Scottish estates where heavy investments have been made to keep a resource available or else much enlarged. But the exemplary resource in this regard has been, and remains, water, for it has been upon water's provision that the greatest sums expended on any resource have been spent.

Yet this may not be an especially good example for proving how man has realized he gets nothing free and must, instead, invest heavily in order to secure a predictable supply. In lieu of regarding water as a free gift of nature, it comes to be regarded as a gift of the state. In ancient civilizations the organization of the water supply was handled by the priests. This was true originally in Sumer and in Egypt and probably in India and China, if indeed in those times it would be feasible to separate the functions of king and priest. At various times between 4000 and 2000 B.C., these four civilizations undertook to mobilize the labor capital for the control of water in order to increase greatly the gross national product.

In Egypt it was the distribution of the annual inundation of the Nile, in China flood control, in Mesopotamia and India irrigation from stream diversions. These were the basis of the later wealthy and powerful cultures historians have called hydraulic civilization. But these projects were undertaken under divine mandates; and the

works that these efforts produced later came to be regarded by these essentially ahistorical cultures as if they
were heavenly gifts to be taken for granted. The result,
where the water resource lacked self-renewing properties, meant the destruction of those civilizations. Not
even god kings, it turned out, could make free gifts on so
magnificent a scale.

The passing of such religious beliefs has transferred
the expectations to the power of the state. It has become
routine for localities to acquire from the general fund of
the central government monies to build structures for
drainage, irrigation, and flood control. Federally, the
American government's initiatory statutes for undertaking
these measures are the Mississippi Valley Commission
Act of 1879, the Rivers and Harbors Act of 1889, the Reclamation Act of 1902, and the Flood Control Act of 1936.
These, and the successor acts, provide for direct expenditures from the federal treasury. At an earlier date,
Congress had sought to use the public lands rather than
cash in the Swamp Lands Act of 1850 and the Desert
Lands Act of 1877 to accomplish the same purposes a
more money-affluent later age carried out by spending
federal revenues or pledging federal credit. The tradition
in water resources is always toward a growth potential in
expenditure level guaranteed to outrun the fiscal resources of the bestowing governmental unit, whatever its
wealth or size.

It has become natural for persons contemplating federal expenditures to dismiss the ability of any particular
project to earn its costs directly from its own operations.
Cost-benefit ratio analyses are done as a matter of law;
but they are not always analyses able to stand up to very
rigorous examination on many occasions. The tendency
has been to put interest rates unrealistically low and to
be generous in income estimates. The idea of multiple
uses has been increasingly popular over the past forty
years, although many ecologists are disenchanted about
the effects of these multifarious constructions, particularly the demands connected with hydropower. But hydropower is nearly always an integral part of these projects because it is in the sale of electricity that projects

can repay costs. In addition this enables low charges to be levied for sale of water and, generally, no charge to made for aiding navigation. The project is regarded as justified further by the employment its construction and maintenance give and by any help it renders a local economy. To ask more is to risk being accused of an ignorance concerning the role of the treasury in a modern economy.

Advocates of this viewpoint buttress their argument by pointing to the military and space expenditures. The most magnificent water proposals may be comparable but plans for all other resource protection are not. They also say the water proposals may generate a reearning capacity, whereas the military and space expenditures cannot similarly affect nature.

In addition it can be seen that the military expenditures are part of the massive drafts being made upon nature, which are creating the potential ecologic catastrophe. Given this situation, the proponents of vast water schemes refuse to be embarrassed by their economics but, instead, justify themselves by what has been done for thirty years for the defense establishment. If the government can afford to spend money without a chance of a directly earned return upon the military and space programs, runs this argument, then the same can be done for water projects.

the demands upon the general fund

It is not easy, of course, to compete for the federal dollar with national defense; and it has proven very difficult, in an economy heated by inflationary pressures, to add costly domestic programs onto a heavy defense budget. Yet even if the costs of these water programs should be transferred from defense, the amounts needed may still prove to be large enough to produce a pause before inaugurating them. Assuredly no one need think that the sums involved are in any way meager.

A commonly urged water transfer project, designed to meet the threatened water famine in the American

Southwest, is the North American Water and Power Alliance. NAWAPA, being the acronym by which it is known, would divert water from the Yukon and Mackenzie rivers and send it down across the North American land mass to empty any residue in the Gulf of California. On the way it would be used for irrigation, refining, pollution control, building up water tables, and similar benefits. Ecologists are fearful of this lowering of the temperature of the Arctic Ocean, of the saturation of ground that has not known water in quantity in modern geologic times, and of the effect on climate of so much water evaporating in normally low-moisture areas. Assuming, however, that all these fears could be answered optimistically, one of the common figures given for the principal sum needed to construct NAWAPA is $100 *billion.* The point is made that this is a government work project on the grand scale comparable to the space program and some of the individual defense operations.

Like them its initial cost would come from the general fund rather than from charges on its beneficiaries. As to maintenance, whose costs have not as yet been capable of estimation, and the hope of earning back any part of the construction outlays, it is power sales upon which reliance will be put, the traditional way of paying for such endeavors. As for the water, it would either be used without charge, as in refilling water tables, or sold for a price really nominal. Probably, too, a period of up to a century would be assigned as the time for repayment, a span economic only for governments.

Of course, one ought not to think this the only large program put forward to bring water to the arid interior. Costs of desalination are figured as at the plant. But thereafter energy pumpers and thousands of miles of pipe are required to raise the desalined water from the sea shore to where it could be used. If such water should be pumped from the Gulf of Mexico to the Southwest, there would have to be added the cost of storage reservoirs to equalize pressure on the line and to install detention basins or injection wells so as to not have the impacted lands of an arid or semiarid territory overwhelmed by the imported water. No one has calculated the full cost of all this, but if projected on the scale of NAWAPA, surely the sum total would be huge.

The legitimation for such investments is the threat to the maintenance of the economy in the dry parts of the United States, stretching from the beginnings of the prairies nearly to the Pacific and from the Mexican to the Canadian border. Early map makers had a habit of scrawling across this zone on the map the words "Great American Desert." Perhaps they were more accurate than later generations.

First grazing and then dry farming on an enormous scale were pursued. These quickly used up whatever moisture the quickly fading perennial grass had held in the soil. Because of high rates of evaporation, it is not easy to accumulate from the erratic rainfall enough reservoir capacity to irrigate in quantity, so the settlers, instead, began to draw on underground sources. In this region much of the ground water is not capable of replenishment, sometimes not even by injection, so that pumping mines the water as much as if it were oil and gas. Even where the water layers are self-replenishing, however, water tables have fallen drastically, with lifting expenses rising and the water coming up being more mineral in content.

A rich, urban-industrial civilization has deliberately been built there; and although toward the northern stretches population has been stable for two generations, the southern end has been in a settlement boom since 1940. Population in the western United States has not tended to settle where water is in ample supply. The confidence that water will somehow be supplied has prevented the appearance in the American Southwest of all the tricks to conserve water developed by the Israelis. Cistern reservoirs, conduit ditches, furrows turned over water, and other methods expensive of capital and labor have rarely been used. A few simple corrections like ripping the water-absorbing vegetation out of the ditches or covering artificial lakes with a thin film of aesthetically pleasing blue oil to reduce evaporation have been made; but more than this has been very hard to persuade irrigators to try. The attitude has been that present need and the prospect of its rapid acceleration cause such efforts to be merest makeshifts. Instead, they gamble that the general fund of the federal government will bring enormous volumes of water from elsewhere.

Throughout the twentieth century within the region, controversy has been carried on between the zones with the water and those with the population. For this reason, as well as fiscal ones, the federal government has to be present in water transfer schemes, although California's multimillion dollar Feather River project is an intrastate sort. But whoever does it, water has to be brought in; and the cost of doing so has been beyond the financial reach of the region to be benefited, no matter how generously its frontiers were drawn.

*the genuine
interests of
the general fund*

It is apparent that, whatever the wisdom of locating population centers in deserts, the United States could not now allow this area to go to ruin for lack of water. It must be brought from somewhere, even if this does intensify the vulnerability of a highly artificial society and increase its dependence on the federal government. Whether the waters come from the Arctic or ocean desalination plants, it must be brought in. Ecologic or even economic intelligence being put aside, politics will not allow of a different solution, so long as the national economy has the viability to bear the cost. To preserve the arid West, after all, acts to reinforce the national market just as, conversely, allowing it to sink would work a market contraction. At least some of what the federal government puts in must be of benefit to the rest of the nation by preserving so large a section of the national economic structure.

Yet this necessary federal participation, drawn from the credit and, ultimately, resources of the rest of the country must not be used by the beneficiaries as if nature had been replaced by the general fund. Just as the local natural resources were broken by this attitude, so shall be the governmental source of this new natural wealth; and even more important, the larger nature

called into play will finally be as exhausted. If this happens, not much apparent chance will be left to go on to
any other help.

The bankruptcy of governments is as nothing compared with the bankruptcy of renewable resources, and
already the ambitious are looking beyond flowing fresh
Arctic water to the use of the Arctic and Antarctic zones.
A single glacier can hold an equivalent of sixty years'
rainfall for the North American continent; and some
would reduce the polar ice and channel the melt to
human uses. Sending icebergs up the Humboldt Current
to Los Angeles has been one serious proposal and, along
with other imaginative suggestions, may come about; but
such programs ought not to be initiated as a matter of
grace and favor.

However hard it may be in an age of inflationary spiraling, all these costs should be made specific and a part
of the price structure, though this may not be possible
for all resources. Public parks, despite the adoption in
1965 of a national admission stamp, cannot be made
self-sustaining out of income. Because much reforestation is to hold soil, slow runoff, and keep streams from
silting, the costs can all scarcely be earned back out of
timber or pulp sales.

In each of these instances the benefits range far beyond any directly derived income. An insistence on cost
consciousness and specificity must never obscure the
real need for resource protection investments which, otherwise, may be hard to defend if the full scope of the
benefits conferred by them is not considered. But this
cannot legitimate treating any state-financed projects as
replacements for a freely exploited nature. When farmers
in Ohio are having to pay their rural water utilities as
much as two dollars per thousand gallons, the continued
selling of water by the thousand gallons for pennies and
mils in the desert Southwest must be terminated.

*the means of
paying for resource use*

The irreducible fact is that water is not free, neither to
nature nor to the state when it replaces nature. This is

true for all the renewable resources, but most clearly of all for water. Pollutors, despite laws denying them the right, treat any nearby surface-water body as a waste receptacle, hopefully to carry it off to be other people's problem, but in any case to get rid of it for free. The consequences have been streams choked with filth. So serious have river and shore pollution become that in a vague way everyone realizes there is a serious situation that has to be corrected. Again, however, the correction seems to be something the state should do at the general taxpayers' expense.

The idea of effluent charges, calculated on the cost of treatment being allocated to individual pollutors, is fought in most of the world. Germany, whose Ruhr valley developed a charge scheme in 1899, has not adopted it nationally; and despite its success in cleaning up the Ruhr, local industrialists grumble about being put at a cost disadvantage and resolutely fight extending the idea to aerial effluents where it would be just as useful. It seems there is no opposition to cleaning up or protecting man's environment so long as it can appear costless; and because such work is not capable of ever being costless, it is preferred to merge costs in the general tax. The preference remains for others to pay directly the costs created for and by some, under the claim that if the general public does not pay through the general fund, nothing can be done to save the situation. Put in these terms, it is simply not true.

Ultimately, of course, everybody must bear a portion of the costs that benefit the totality of the economy. Sadly, many have no general benefit; and worse than benefiting but a few at general expense, these are the very enterprises most harmful to the ecology. Yet when the ecology or the human economy is benefited, it is unrealistic for a single industry, a few individuals, or a locality to absorb the cost. The general public, too, has been misled into regarding as free resources that clearly are most expensive; and taxes are one means of meeting these costs.

Still, the tax structure is not the sole means of paying those costs. Such matters are, after all, not only integral to maintenance of the human environment but are also specific to the industries connected with the disturbed resources. These disturbances are just as much costs of doing business as the payroll or commodities used in manufacture and are no more suitable than those for passing on to nature or the general credit of the state. Elements like these traditional ones become, instead, a part of the price structure resting on whatever product is being made; and it is in this manner that the expense of maintaining man's environment must also be worked into the price. It is as consumers, rather than as taxpayers, that the general public will bear the cost. Indeed, in an age of sales, excise, customs, and transfer taxes having an increasing popularity, even the general fund itself seeks to make the state revenues appear part of the commodity's price. This being so, it is not a radical step to put such constraints on the market that business must assume these costs and make them a component of the price finally set for sale to the public.

Charges such as these should never be treated as taxes thrust down on the operation of the market. Many, like the reforestation efforts, bring wood products into the market so that dependent forest industries can continue to function. Others, like soil conservation, made an agricultural revolution partly possible. Still others make possible continued industrial production by disposing of its off-fall as do incinerators, land-fills, and septic tanks. The costs of all this have an absolute necessity to the market's continued existence, and to expect the market to defray those costs can scarcely be oppressing it.

Worked into the final price, such costs acquire an economy and specificity lacking when made up from the general fund. There is a world of difference between charging off such items to nature, or to the general taxpayer, and making them part of a firm's cost of doing business. In the latter case they tend to take on a more intense significance to the managers who have to deal with them. Constantly faced with the need to accommodate them, there can be no confusion about how free are the renewable resources employed in the modern urbanindustrial economy.

the values not
expressible in cash

This is not to say that what must be done in setting up a stable balance between man's ambitions and the world wherein he pursues them can be expressed entirely in cash terms. Aesthetics and a conscience reflecting a sense of man's responsibility for the universe are not likely to find their fullest description in a balance sheet. After all, if the pessimists have any measure of accuracy in their predictions of future ecologic catastrophes to the atmosphere, the oceans, the soil, or the vital gases of oxygen and nitrogen as the result of unchecked industrial behavior, then it is man's own salvation that is at issue. Can even the most cash conscious man not find here a value worth preserving, even if money terms do not entirely comprise it?

Every value needed to keep up a viable relationship between man and the ecumene of which he is a part must be questioned. The effort to do so will be tough but it is of the greatest importance. If the economy operated so that no one expected any aspect of the renewable resources to be a free gift from nature or from the general fund of the state, if the economy specified these costs and both expressed in cash terms those aspects capable of such expression and incorporated into the final price whatever could be so included, then what remained would be far simpler to define.

Solutions often reveal greater complexities, but they do not create them. Instead, solutions identify and highlight difficulties that have always been present, although unknown. This doubtless would be true in this instance. The time is certainly long overdue to cease treating natural resources as free gifts, to specify their costs, to integrate these costs into the economic structure as necessary charges, and to incorporate such costs into the price. When this has been done, work will still remain to be carried on to maintain both man and his ecumene. But until this much is accomplished, nothing else can have long-run success.

Any other course is like piling weights on a runner and expecting him to win every race against unhandicapped rivals: Ultimately, whatever his powers, he must fail and, given enough effort under such odds, his failure has the likelihood of being fatal. It would seem that only a very odd mind would set up a race on conditions such as these, nor would it be a mind entitled to much respect or imitation.

REFERENCES

Harold J. Barnett and Chandler Morse, *Scarcity and Growth: The Economics of Natural Resource Availability,* Baltimore: Johns Hopkins, 1963.

Richard A. Cooley, *Politics and Conservation: The Decline of the Alaskan Salmon Fisheries,* New York: Harper & Row, 1963.

Philip Foss, *Politics and Grass: The Administration of Grazing on the Public Domain,* Seattle: University of Washington Press, 1960.

Luther Halsey Gulick, *American Forest Policy: A Study of Government Administration and Economic Control,* New York: Duell, Sloan, & Pearce, 1951.

Jack Hirshleifer, Jerome Milliman, and James De Haven, *Water Supply: Economics, Technology, and Policy* (with Postscript), Chicago: University of Chicago Press, 1969.

Thomson King, *Water: Miracle of Nature,* New York: Collier Books, 1961.

Maurice H. Merrill, *The Public's Concern with the Fuel Minerals,* St. Louis: Thomas Law Book Company, 1960.

Charles F. Park, Jr., with Margaret Freeman, *Affluence in Jeopardy: Minerals and the Political Economy,* San Francisco: Freeman, Cooper & Co., 1968.

Ronald G. Ridker, *Economic Costs of Air Pollution: Studies in Measurement,* New York: Frederick A. Praeger, 1967.

Robert Leo Smith, *Ecology and Field Biology,* New York: Harper & Row, 1966.

5

the legal ways of controlling nature

*the limits on
the criminal sanction*

A very common reaction to any kind of behavior that comes to be regarded as socially unwholesome is for the law to forbid it. Hopefully, by making certain conduct illegal, persons will cease engaging in it; and if they do not stop, their arrest and punishment will reform them and deter others. Although both traditional and popular, some question exists as to how effective a control pure prohibition may be. In the absence of supportive social and economic pressures thrusting in the same direction as the prohibitions and the criminal sanctions, the efficiency is probably quite small.

For example, laws forbidding the setting afire of forests are common. With wood values rising for use as lumber or pulp, with the forest itself becoming a recreational resort possessed of high intrinsic worth on the site, anyone who burns standing timber has both destroyed valuable property and committed a crime assuming steadily more serious proportions with each decade. Such arson is a social offense reaching beyond tree destruction to include animal deaths, disturbance of reproduction or food sources for fire survivors, erosion of soil accumulations, and siltation or flooding of the bottoms. So serious are such fires that not only is it a crime to deliberately set one but it is criminal conduct to behave so recklessly that a blaze ensues or even in certain dry seasons to merely enter parts of the forest. The criminal code reaches beyond the deliberate malefactor to apprehend the careless or the disobedient.

Yet it is not possible to rely purely on the criminal code. Though such conduct is illegal, how many campers who have been careless with fires are arrested each year? How is it possible to arrest every litterer for tossing a cigarette stub out of a car window? And if they are caught, what penalty commensurate with the offense can be levied? Should a conflagration have been the result, even convictions for the resulting deaths of firefighters produce penalties inadequate to the harm done. Perhaps there are campers deterred from negligence by fear of the criminal court, but they are not likely to be a majority.

Instead of stressing the criminal sanction, government in recent decades has tried to build an ecologic conscience. To instill by persuasion the desire not to do harm and an unconsciously conservation-minded behavior has been the governmental purpose. Smokey the Bear as a fire warden, the comic characters of Yogi Bear and his friend Boo-Boo, the Disney cartoons with the small animals showing human emotions before the flames' onslaught, the nature films showing the desolation by fire, have all had their effect. This public education has not stopped forest fires of human origin, but when joined with the rising value of timber, it has reduced their number and their severity.

Unfortunately, depressed economic conditions for populations in forest areas are more the rule than the exception. This is due partly to the fact that forests represent frozen capital assets, partly to the effect forests have of shutting out much human population from areas they cover, and partly to the low employment needs of forest industries, including modern lumbering. Particularly in a cash economy, economic circumstances can be desperate. Consequently, one of the dangers to the forest has been natives setting it afire so that they could get work first as firefighters, then as workmen redressing the damage done to the bottoms by erosion, and finally as the planters of trees in a newly reforested area. Building an ecologic conscience in people like this has no more chance of success than the prospect of punishing them under the criminal law. The best recourse here is to encourage them to emigrate or else to see that they have adequate jobs at home. Only by removal of temptation can acts like these be prevented, for if economic provocation is strong enough, neither general exhortation nor punishment after the event can succeed in protecting the forests.

Such risks are the perils of economic depression in the forest, but rising prices, too, can have a hurtful effect. Lumber prices rose in 1965, not just for hardwood, which long had been the case, but for all woods used regularly in construction. Logs in perfect condition of certain woods in high demand, such as Douglas fir, had reached by the spring of 1969 a price of $125 apiece for cutting. It represented an open invitation to timber thieves, who cruised the woods looking for trees whose species or condition made them prime for market. Regardless of ownership, public or private, these trees were ripped out, with any rarity they possessed simply further assuring them destruction. Persons owning land with trees of this kind on them were pressured into cutting them for several reasons: They could pocket the money themselves; their own cutting might not damage the less valuable stands; and their harvest would economize on any subsequent reforestation. No motives other than greed control the timber thieves, who shivvy even state-owned forests into having their trees brought to market sooner than when ready. Indeed, the forests most imperiled are those never meant for commercial cutting either because they are intended for recreational use or lie on ground not suitable for tree cycling.

So severe can timber theft become that during periods of high prices booms of logs are stolen in operations requiring many men and hours of labor. Because the thieves need sawmills, especially where the tree has been marked with an owner's brand, forest managers use informers to reveal secret sawmills and logging trails or to denounce sawmills fencing the cut timber. The lumber companies have preferred to set up their own systems of spies and enforcers rather than to rely on the criminal law. Rarely will they prosecute, partly to prevent revenge fires or sabotage, partly because timber thieves often have local friends in the local system of justice, and partly because there is considerable safety in knowing who the thieves are, where they cut, how they haul, and to whom they sell. With knowledge such as this the legitimate owner can go further in protecting his growing stands than if he runs to the sheriff. Prosperity clearly brings different problems than depression, but so far as nature is concerned the consequence need not differ much in the extent of the harm wrought.

the use of wardens
to protect resources

The same kind of reasoning applies to the success of that most traditional of all law enforcement officers, the fish and game warden. His history is a very ancient one in the assertion of the king's right to exclude anyone not holding the royal license from taking fish or game. However, so unpopular was this control over game by the Crown that in 1788 one of the propositions urged for the Bill of Rights in the new United States Constitution was the forbidding of the federal government from interfering with the taking of game. Though it failed, there was no effective, and little formal, control over the taking of game. Not even private landowners had the temerity to exclude hunters, and the ability of private landowners to effectively post their premises against poachers was one of the first limitations upon the unrestricted taking of game.

Despite popular opposition, however, the positions of fish and game and forest wardens were created—or re-created, if history is cited—during the last third of the nineteenth century. Their number has increased, as have the budgets supporting them; but as their importance has grown, their jobs have been diversified. Though patrol is still important, they have other duties that are more concerned with stimulating and channeling public use of the facilities they are guarding. The task is less one of apprehending offenders than conditioning public users. Without this prior direction to guide individuals, enforcement would be overwhelmed. The latter still has importance, of course, for there are those who can never be conditioned toward lawful conduct to any sort of natural resource.

Neither should it be forgotten that the places where poachers, timber thieves, and illegal seiners operate can be very lonely indeed for a confrontation between them and one or two wardens. The sort of person who will dynamite a pond for the fish, seek out doe and fawn for the tenderer meat gourmets prefer, or cull out others' trees as price leads him is not at all reluctant to deal ruthlessly with any informer or police officer who threatens his activities.

Nor does a certain secret envy fail to excite a degree of sympathy for these criminals' allegedly "free" way of life. It is a mistaken sympathy, however, since their vaunted independence is a myth. The fact that prompts their depredations and causes them to reach levels of great damage is the market. It stimulates them and gives them insatiable goals, so that they are entitled to as little sympathy as a lumber baron skinning off a mountain range. The motives are the same and the public's finer feelings should be reserved for the isolated wardens who have to cope with people of such ilk.

Truly, though, if most of those going into the forests did it illegally to despoil them, nothing could prevent them from doing so. Assuming government would bother with wardens if most of its society held such views, no possible force could prevent the forest and all within it from being taken and ultimately destroyed. In north Africa, where the French colonialists engaged in considerable reforestation, it is proving impossible to exclude timber takers, charcoal burners, and herds from the groves. In east Africa the natives since independence cannot everywhere be compelled to observe the limits of the game preserves.

Research on population shifts in east and south Africa shows that the arrival of the Bantu, with their cattle culture, has occurred since the seventeenth century; and the destruction of ground cover, soil, and water can be attributed to the introduction of these great herds. The people, however, go on increasing their herds, despite the harm to the land and a resultant deteriorating effect on the herds. There are wardens working to protect resources in these regions, some of them under well-conceived programs, but in the absence of public support such efforts cannot have much success.

poverty's burden on natural resources

An area can be so lacking in economic choices, with population pressing hard on resources, that little can be done to protect it even for further exploitation. The sort of direct use that has been so destructive in parts of the world as widely separated as northern China, east Africa, and Appalachia is possibly the most harmful of all, for it fails to build up a surplus out of which might be financed the development of a common ecologic conscience.

A more sophisticated processing of the environment causes great harm. But in so doing, it provides a means to work a reversal if man truly wants to control the environment of which he is a part. When regions are threatened with extirpation of trees, grass, wildlife, or soil because the people there need them for immediate conversion to food, then there is no means to reverse the condition within a situation of steadily increasing resource exhaustion.

It is very fashionable to say that much of the world, still using stone tools and charred pointed sticks for agricultural implements, will have to skip the stage of the modern agricultural revolution and go directly to an industrial synergizing of food. This is said because its fields are exhausted, fertilizer cannot be produced in needed amounts, and production is capable of little growth for the countryside is unable to respond to the demand for food without an investment these economies find impossible to make. Possibly, if they were prepared to forego industrial investment, rural conditions might improve; but this is meant to provide the capital surplus so badly needed and to meet the domestic demands for an urban type of existence that increasing numbers of their people crave. It is easy to say that the investment should be diverted to agriculture. Yet no state has yet built a secure capital base for its economy out of agricultural goods; and so some problem solvers urge that this stage be skipped entirely.

However, the source of the investment for this exponential leap into the future is just as lacking as it is for any other purpose. Perhaps assistance might come from outside, but it is not likely to come on the scale needed. In Macao, the Portuguese have started a reforestation project on the two larger islands that already provides a pleasant recreation spot for visitors from Hong Kong and Macao City. Soon they will actually be able to engage in lumbering on a small scale. The Chinese islands around these remain brown and bleak; and it would scarcely be possible for the Chinese government to make the investment that has been feasible for the Portuguese at Macao.

Even the outside assistance coming into these countries, whether as purchases, loans, or gifts, has too often not been for investment but for a subsistence consumption, from which only a little time can be bought rather than a base prepared for change. Valiant efforts have been made to use labor as the capital, so that it is suggested organizing it into communes in order to create the needed surplus by being simultaneously productive both agriculturally and industrially. Whatever the risks to nature threatened by, and to, the active urban-industrial economies, there is capital within those economies with which their social and legal structures can finance techniques of control and restoration. The same possibilities are not present in those countries caught in an urban-industrial world and yet lacking the economies capable of producing the surplus so necessary to it.

the practical
consequence of
ecologic conscience

The bases for effective legal protection of natural re-sources rest on a widely held opinion of their importance and also sufficient economic strength to finance needed programs. Nature is so vulnerable to man's demands on it that there is no force able to prevent such harm. Only an inner mechanism of restraint, acting as a social con-science forbidding the individual to perpetrate certain acts, can protect resources that so often lie in remote, uninhabited, and unprotectable places.

Indeed, when the statute books know only criminal sanctions and when little effort is put into their enforce-ment, the law becomes a matter for humor. This was the treatment given the fish, game, and forest wardens in the United States for decades. Humorists depicted them as gumshoes sneaking up on shrewd rustics at their fishing and hunting pleasures, who consistently outtricked the stupid officers at what was only, after all, a comic game. Considering what these men were paid, the duties they were assigned, and the territories nominally within their jurisdiction, the whole institutional setup could only have been taken as a joke.

Yet joke or no, these few men were the means toward a program of forest and wildlife management. Through the fish-stocking programs begun by the State Fisheries Commission of Wisconsin in the 1870s, the first evidence was accumulated of the water conditions needed by dif-ferent kinds of fish for both life and breeding. By the 1890s they knew enough of bio-oxygen demand to know why fish died in polluted but nontoxic water. They had learned, too, why certain streams historically had one sort of fish rather than another and why species pre-ferred by sport fishermen could not always flourish.

Yet though all this has now been known for decades, there are those who insist that state stocking of streams is the answer to diminishing or changing fish popula-tions. For example, a veteran's organization in order to sponsor a national fish-catching contest in June, 1969, for over one thousand youngsters stocked a Colorado stream the day before. When the time came for the contest, all the fish were dead, and "pollution" was blamed. Perhaps pollution was the culprit, but even pollution is a more complex idea than the sponsors of this contest seem to be aware; and that is more sad than funny after a century of work by state fish commissions and their wardens and researchers.

the full
burden of wardenship

It is hard today to realize how humble were the origins in the United States of the resource protection agencies. The first federal forest ranger station was built in 1898 by some of the few rangers out of their own meager incomes; and to read the accounts of their work is to be deeply impressed. Just the miles of trails ridden on horseback, many of the trails built by them, make an impact on anyone who has ever jolted along the same way.

That first ranger station caught the public imagination; and for over half a century forest rangers were regarded as men in fire towers, with no other functions worth financing. Certainly their work against forest fires has been important; and the reduction in the damage done by these conflagrations has been due substantially to the wardens, especially those in the federal forest service. It was even necessary for them to invent around 1912 the special sort of ax needed in forest fires, to develop the technique of the counterfire, to begin the use in 1939 of parachutes for firefighters, to inaugurate the program educating the mass of users who have invaded the parks and forests since the Korean War about the risks of fire, and to do whatever has been needed to protect a diminishing and overused resource against the wanton destruction that fire so often represents. Too often firewatching has been seen as the entirety of the wardens' duties; and this is most unfortunate at a time when more men are being freed for other duties by the use of remote-control warning devices. The public must see the forest warden as having other important protective duties.

Not the least of these is working against disease. Trees in North America had no natural resistance to diseases common and perhaps mild elsewhere. Given the closeness with which man lives in the world in the twentieth century, the spread of disease is inevitable. Efforts to confine tree and plant blights have rarely been successful, despite road blocks, searches, and confiscations. Painful episodes, such as persons trying to eat a bushel of oranges at the barrier so that they will not be "wasted" by confiscation, have ensued; but generally the blights have spread.

For instance, outside of managed forests, as a result of ruthless past cutting and the blight of the chestnut and elm, is the beech. No one has given it any special protection but it is tough, thus far resistant to disease, and without commercial value, all of which have enabled it to replace other species. Unfortunately, certain insects acclimated to the leaves of other trees have had a hard time readjusting to the beech, with the result that lesser forest life has been put under stress; but for purposes of ground cover and stream siltation it is fortunate that the beech prospered. The moral from the point of view of enforcing law in the forest is, of course, that one must work with the strongest natural forces during a readjustment to catastrophe unless one has the knowledge and the means to restore artificially the precatastrophe situation.

Too often, when dealing with nature rather than human law violators, force has been used to solve problems which might have responded favorably to some solution that did not call for extermination or total alteration of preexisting relationships. But the direct forceful means has generally seemed the cheapest, swiftest, easiest, and hence best way of dealing with the difficulty. If any sort of insect is a disease carrier or simply a nuisance, a program of spraying to eliminate it is started. The fact that the other species which fed on the one attacked may be even more effectively eliminated has not been given enough consideration. The setting up of more encompassing solutions simply has not been a task assigned lawyers by the social, political, and economic managers. The full burden of wardenship has been avoided in this manner.

the variety in
enforcement of
resource protection

William McChesney Martin, the former chairman of the Federal Reserve Bank System, has suggested a means of financing necessary natural resource projects despite the charge so often made that the money cannot be found to pay for them. The proposal he has made is a program of compulsory saving from income with the accumulated fund being invested in resource projects. Naturally, since he is a banker suggesting this device as a way to soak up inflation and is concerned with a high return, his recommended investment is hydropower, which scarcely qualifies as a resource improvement to conservationists. But there is no reason not to diversify these investments, even though this might reduce the return on the invested money. Indeed, in less developed economies it has long been a possibility to make the same monies do double duty by employing sums deducted from payroll for social security as investments in social purposes capable of earning a direct return in cash profits. There is, therefore, nothing particularly radical about the idea.

Yet over the years it has proven hard to carry the concept into effect. Political resistance to it runs high, for some prefer payment through taxes to any programs of enforced savings and politicians like the unallocated in preference to the specific appropriation. It is, however, an alternative to be put forward seriously whenever the opposition to natural resource protection states that the money to carry it out is not to be found in a period of inflation, military or domestic unrest, or broad retrenchment in general government expenditure.

The reason for such a concern under challenge is that the law ought to be a means of solving problems. Very often, however, it seems to be a way of preventing their solution; but this is due either to a partially obscured view, which cannot see the problems being solved, or else to a failure of legal institutions to function to any minimal degree. When persons attack lawyers as being responsible for the destruction of the human environment because their advice assists the industries doing the harm, they are right—to a degree. But it must not be forgotten that imperial China, though it did not have the profession of lawyer, still managed to do great harm through deforestation and careless soil use, and it has intensified the effects of floods in two of its great valleys, the Hwang Ho and the Yangtze, through the work of the ancient ministry of water conservancy. It is not the lawyer who is most culpable, for the harm would exist without him; he is not the final arbiter; and at his professional worst, his harm comes from the edge rather than the center.

Yet lawyers cannot beg off with this exculpation, because they can use the courts as instruments of law enforcement, persuasion, and education. This does not mean filing law suits to get publicity for a special cause or to pressure the legislature. Inventing litigation to vex and to make propaganda, however noble the objective, would be an abuse of process. But the statute books have many laws relating to environmental protection which have not been enforced because no one has cared to apply them, or they are cumbersome, or public officials have been indifferent. In addition, general rules of law, which have application in the environmental area, may have been ignored because previous conditions had not shown how they could be applied in new areas. Class actions by citizens' groups, private suits for nuisance and trespass, punitive damages, prayers for bonds to enforce decrees, are only a few examples.

The Environmental Defense Fund has put lawyers in motion to enforce quiescent statutes, to galvanize administrative agencies and prosecutors, and to extend general legal rules to ecologic problems. There is, for example, a rule that one using a dangerous instrumentality is absolutely liable for any harm that results while he is using it. The difficulty in court arises, of course, out of the determination of what is a dangerous instrumentality. But if an instrument is dangerous enough, not only is its user liable for harm done, but he can be prohibited from using it in the future. A legislature can do this by statute; an administrative agency can do it by order; or it can be done by a court injunction. The Environmental Defense Fund, in the exemplary case of pesticides like DDT and other chlorinated hydrocarbons, has taken the position that there is now enough accumulated evidence to show the inherent menace, that great damage has been done, and that further use should be enjoined. To this end, suits have been filed and positive results reached in court in several states, including Michigan and Wisconsin.

the reason for law's reluctance to prohibit

Judges have not shown themselves willing to issue injunctions, which have the drastic effect of terminating activities permanently prohibited. Some individuals in pesticide cases have had better luck with damage actions for harm done to later crops planted after a herbicide has been sprayed on an earlier one. But victory has not been common in these instances either, because of defenses that claim the warnings were adequate or the manufacturer had no way of knowing their full potential or the unfortunate results were due to intervening causes. Any one of these can be very hard to rebut.

If suits such as these have proven hard to win, claims asserting human damage from chlorinated hydrocarbons have been nearly impossible. Evidence shows they accumulate in tissues, particularly in the productive organs; but whereas in other species their effect has ranged from sterilization to toxic deaths, to this point similar results have not been clinically established in humans. Though many fear these chemicals will accumulate and that the effect would be cancer-inducing, a lawyer cannot make his case out of fears, not even scientific ones, until enough statistics accumulate to approach certainty.

So far, as an example, courts have not rendered judgments against cigarette makers on behalf of persons claiming to have contracted lung cancer, emphysema, circulatory disease, and renal failure through smoking them. Many doctors are satisfied that a cause-effect relationship between cigarette smoking and these illnesses has been established. But judges and juries either believe the proof insufficient to support a heavy damage recovery or that the smoker assumed a risk for whose adverse effect he must now be prepared to suffer.

Yet this should not be discouraging, because the facts are building up continuously. Suits concerning environmental harm have an influence on the public attitude which runs outside the courtroom. The Environmental Defense Fund has not been satisfied with law suits or petitions in chancery for injunctions. It has pursued the routes of hearings before administrators and legislative committees in order to secure the issuance of more stringent regulations and the passage of more comprehensive legislation, respectively. Coordinating the processes of courts, administrative agencies, and legislatures in order to accomplish change has a fairly old history. The reason this is necessary is that courts are not central to the power contained in any social structure. They give their approval, instead, to decisions already agreed on over a wide social spectrum.

When in times of drastic social change the courts serve as crisis makers, their decisions either express agreed-upon conclusions acceptable to society or they do not. When they do not, when there is both an insufficient majority to produce a constitutional change and yet a significant minority that will not recede, the issue spills out of the bounds of constitutional order into civil tumult or civil war in order to reach the final public settlement. Clearly, only issues of great significance, able to mobilize popular opinion, can force such confrontations.

the mobilization
of public opinion
to protect nature

For good or ill, protection or destruction of the environment does not seem to produce the commitments race, religion, nationality, and class have been able to instigate. The passion so common to these is not available; and while this is regrettable to those trying so hard to mobilize support to protect nature, it is well it is lacking in those destroying it. Though ignorance, apathy, greed, selfishness, and stupidity are all serious enemies to change, they come nowhere near the effectiveness of a bigotry not particularly wound up in an awareness of private advantage.

Against an attitude that honestly justifies itself in terms of some ideal of progress, efforts to preserve the environment beat like waves along a rocky shore. What must be done in such instances is to identify the progress sought, reveal the harms wrought, isolate the special interests, show the alternative ways of reaching desired goals that do minimal harm to the environment, and perhaps even persuade society to prefer goals with less demand on nature. It is in the accomplishing of these ends that those interested in protecting nature must work. The drama of insurrection and civil war are lacking, though an occasional demonstration may be employed. Extensive change will have to come out of steady, persistent efforts to create viable rather than deteriorating balances between man and his environment.

The main course of change must be through the legislature and must lie with those who formulate controlling views in society at large. The law must act within its broadest definition, setting up institutions in balance with the environment in as nearly a self-operating manner as possible. Specifications of needs and their costs, as well as their accumulation into the price structure, are necessities to break the old fascination with nature as a free good and to free the general fund of the weight of this vital work. It is the job of the law not only to see that what must be done is accomplished, but that it is done in a way to minimize resistance. If the law can get work done without the awareness that its performance is anything other than simple, self-sustained routine, the legal process has functioned successfully. The law can do this only when there is general agreement on goals; and when this is lacking, the law is on its way to failure as the public is made grindingly aware of how the mechanism interlocked in its act of falling apart.

In a time when the size and the technological character of the world civilization require larger and more complex systems to deal with the changing situations, and when simultaneously there is widespread discontent approaching rebellion over the impersonality and considerable individual injustices of already existing systems of control, it is the law's duty to reconcile these needs and aspirations. If the law fails, the whole mechanism will likely fly to fragments under an intolerable strain. Society's needs and hopes produce crises; and it is the job of the law to channel the energy contained in these situations so as to make productive the goals desired in the conflicting positions, or to do it as nearly as the contending forces will allow. For the law simply to allow endless sequences of violent confrontation is to have abdicated its role in the social relationship.

Legal process must be employed at the very center of controversy if the final disposition of affairs is to be other than a matter of naked power. To stay at the edge of things is to be ineffective and possibly ridiculous. Where the problem is gravest and the point where its cause lies are the places where legal activity belongs. Everything else merely plays at dealing with difficulties.

the utility of market constraints in conservation law

There are some who would leave all resource regulation to the free operation of the market, on the basis that scarcity confers a value which the market will prolong. There is much truth in this; and one can see that values tend to be priced in terms of scarcity and demand. But the market does not always act perfectly, and it is the law's function to set constraints on the market so that the imperfections can be favorably accounted for.

Demand can be a transient matter. Scarcity can make even the market hurry along a resource's destruction, as happened at the last to the buffalo in a market demanding robes and horn furniture. When transportation costs are high or labor supply is scarce, the market will draw on the low-quality resources; and when prices go high enough, wholly unsuitable resources will be brought into the market, as when high grain prices plowed up and produced the Dust Bowl.

The market must be worked with by the law, just as

the forces of the environment must not be worked against by the law's enforcement process. But the market, like nature itself, cannot be left to its own devices when demand conditions reach the sort of situations where producers can switch off costs to nature or the state. The law cannot allow this ducking of responsibilities; and it must be used to set the constraints within which the market will exploit nature and nature can recover itself from this exploitation.

The criminal sanction is a part of this procedure, but so also are the setting of standards, the suggestion of criteria, education, persuasion, the use of subsidies, the rebate of taxes, preferences for specific products, and charge schemes meant to do anything from covering the cost of redressing some specific harm to making uneconomic the practice causing it. One example relates to fuel with a high sulphur content. Though cheaper in price, it can cause not only air pollution but damage to the fabric of buildings, to paint, and to human tissue. It is, therefore, a nuisance made worse by its low cost.

The law could take one of several approaches. It might forbid its use, under criminal penalty, using a chemical monitoring system to seek out offenders. It might educate the public to the hidden costs, or set minimal standards for sulphur content in all fuel sold in bulk, or require smoke control devices for extracting the sulphur, or set up subsidies to help owners use more expensive fuels or give a tax preference to those who do, or tax the high-sulphur fuels until they are as expensive as those with low sulphur content. Which of these is used will be determined by the available technology, the prosperity of the local economy, or the level of administrative expertise; but what cannot pass unchallenged is the statement that the law does not have available a wide variety of remedies.

the role of the
administrative agency

Techniques exist that do not require the administrative agency which seems modern society's only answer to its problems and which is commonly regarded as sitting in remote and unconcerned judgment on the individual citizen in whatever he wants to do. If ineffectiveness of the criminal sanction induces contempt, ineffectiveness in the administrative processes produces the hatred born of continuous frustration. Both reactions can only impair law's effectiveness, for the sanction and the administrative process are necessary means of enforcing at a public level what society wants its members to do. In a world as complexly exploited as the contemporary one is, only subtle and far-reaching acts of public administration can provide the needed control, machinery for changes, and regimes for maintaining both a technological civilization and a viable environment for it to function in. To dismiss the administrative process as an invention from a Kafka novel would be as sad as construing all police work in terms of Mack Sennett's Keystone Kops.

The administrative method is needed to preserve man and his environment in a world economy where governmental expenditures play an increasingly larger part, regardless of whether the industrial forms are private or state capitalist enterprises. With the financing coming directly or indirectly from the public treasury, the government can lay down the ecologic terms on which it is to be done, just as it has required certain safety devices on equipment, use of union labor, lack of racial discrimination, insurance, and performance bonds, as well as the technical adequacy called for in the specifications for the bidding. To require as well preplanned schemes for handling erosion during construction, or closed systems for waste disposal, definitely amounts to no administrative revolution.

Although the problems raised by the urban-industrial economy are world-wide, massive administrative agencies are not the sole answer. Indeed, there must be sufficient interaction between regulators and regulated to trigger among the latter the self-regulating machanism so essential to getting most of the work done. There should not be so much control that the economy cannot sustain its heavy burden, nor should there be so much that the burden of responsibility could be shunted onto the controllers.

It is at the specific, local level, among private and particular enterprises, that the ecologic accounting must take place. Since most individual enterprises are lacking in sufficient wherewithal to go it alone in resource matters, local agencies can be created to build sewers, waste treatment plants, or rural water supply; and when the size of the job grows too large for them, they can join with similarly situated entities in joint operations or be merged into a regional association on a broader scale. The agencies doing the work may be as local as the present-day sanitation departments, but they will be part then of a vast operation to which they will owe an unshirkable duty.

Indeed, despite the need for incorporating ecologic salvation into the production process and for community control, there still cannot be a total delegation to local or industrial entities. Such a location of this power has in the past produced too little because the advantage lies mostly in passing off responsibility and the lowest level of performance tends to become the norm. There has to be something beyond the purely local to carry information from one to another, to show each there are others, to carry on research, to require steadily higher performances, and to integrate otherwise minimally significant fragments into a unity capable of making a positive effect.

At a time when it is feared the runoff from DDT may interfere as much as 75 percent with the photosynthesis performed by plankton, supplying the planet's oceans with oxygen, it is evident a township constable, or county pest control officer, or even state pesticide board is not of sufficient jurisdictional scope to have an adequate choice at solution. So dependent has agriculture in many areas become on chlorinated hydrocarbons that something—whether biological or chemical—must be found to replace them if there are not to be severe regional dislocations.

the chances
of local initiative

Localities can help themselves as well as the general condition, as New York City has done since 1966 with its air pollution control ordinance which has helped air quality by reducing the sulphur content. This improves the amenity of city life; and ultimately air conditions in the city will require regulation of the several interrelated air sheds in the metropolitan region, without any exemptions being tolerated. Compared to the larger difficulty of heat pollution in the earth's atmosphere, this may seem small; but a beginning must be made to cope with the effects of burning fossil fuels on the world's atmosphere which has been accelerating by the decades since 1900 on an exponential scale without any sign of diminishing as yet.

Perhaps material improvements in the world situation could be made if the localities where crisis conditions are at their worst would simply try to save themselves without waiting for the greater action of others. Because the crises come in localities of the greatest productivity, it would seem this is where the resources would be to make restoration possible. Unfortunately, New York City, to continue with it as an example, received back as of 1969 only $3 billion of the $14 billion its enterprise paid in taxes to the federal and state governments. In addition all the problems other than the ecologic that result from the demands of urban-industrial society also concentrate in these centers and make their drafts on the proceeds earned, making nature compete with the needs to redress man's own human dislocation. Politically, these last become preferable, for nothing in nature votes or receives relief or collects dividends or gathers hospital benefits.

Yet the pressure is rising at the local level, for it is there that the amenities first shift from being unpleasant to perilous; and it is the personal, local level rather than the universal condition on which man has his awareness of living. Until he is engaged here and at this point starts the reversal of what is unviable in the balance between himself and nature, then all other plans, however meritorious the purposes, will have inadequate successes. And in the state of today's accelerating world demands, caused by joining a population explosion to a revolution of expectancy within a technological culture, inadequate becomes irrelevant unless it is the threshold of needed change.

the immediate
and ultimate
needs for legal change

Ancient antecedents can be found for courses the law must take to control what humanity demands of its environment. However, it would be an error to do more than point out their existence, for what must take place now is the realization that drastic changes impend. A balance is needed in the world's ecology and legal process must fully assume that responsibility.

There will have to be an administration of artificial regimes to replace the natural means rivers have for purging and straightening themselves, or soil has for rebuilding itself, or wildlife has for reproducing, or air has for replenishing its elements. These need not all be done by externally imposed constraints or by criminal fines and terms of imprisonment. Impersonality, alienation, and remoteness need not mark the law's role in ecologic control. Means for integrating the solution into the problem, for specifying the cost of the difficulty and of its removal, exist conceptually and can be called into legal being. All that is needed is the realization of the danger and the will to assume the responsibility for coping with all of its ramifications.

The realization has appeared in legal circles. From the United Nations, which is to hold a conference in 1972 on the crisis in the environment, through various national governments and concerned pressure groups, to the garbage committees of town councils, there has had to be a level of concern lacking in the past. The law is responding to this realization with a wide range of measures going much beyond anything regularly or generally used before.

The growing legal effect is so much in evidence, some people already think it to be enough. When he signed the Water Quality Act of 1965, President Johnson hailed it as the end of a long struggle. That it was; but more important, it was the beginning of a new one. His own signature on the Water Resources Research Act and the Clean Waters Restoration Act of 1966 and the Wild Rivers Act of 1968 proved that, as do the continuing struggles to fund and strengthen them. The Santa Barbara channel incident of the fractured oil well, which began an ecologic agony in January, 1969, quickly showed the failures of the Clean Waters Act and the need for its amendment. Funding, too, for such work is constantly undermined by economizers, so that federal financing of water quality programs in 1969 ran at only about 20 percent of a minimal level of support; and just as federal funding stimulates state, local, and private effort, cutting it back collapses these efforts as well. Although the problem is in its maturity, the task of asserting sufficient control to shift the trend from destruction to viability is in its infancy. The institutions to perform the task are many of them in being, which was not true even in 1960, but they are still weak compared to the need for strength that the work commands by reason of the risks posed.

There is no reason for satisfaction with the control situations. Every time such an emotion has appeared in the past, as evidenced by the century-long history of water pollution control in Wisconsin, a crisis was at hand and what was needed was a deepening of the control process. Administrators, far from wanting to extend their scope, tend most to fear making enemies, which leads them normally to pursue very passive policies that will neither threaten what they have nor upset others into change. The impetus for change, though deriving its information or even its goal from the work of the agency, is generally some pressure group more upset by what has not been accomplished than soothed by the old bromide "Think how much worse things would be if what has been done had not happened." Those wanting change are quite right to demand far more and to take expressions of satisfaction as premature. The greatest successes of the control agencies so far have been skirmishes in a far larger campaign; and satisfaction in such victories, if more than fleeting, is always misplaced.

Change, when confined to the terms of present conduct, is frequently not sufficient. For example, because of the risks of chlorinated hydrocarbons to warm-blooded creatures, pesticides of sulphurated hydrocarbons have been developed that so far as can be determined cannot harm them. But a spill in June, 1969, killed over 40 million fish in the Rhine, for fish find the substance paralyzing to their breathing organs. Clearly the change-over from one hydrocarbon to another is not sufficient and the parameters of needed change have not been drawn widely enough.

In technical and in legal areas alike the options for reversing the trends in resource destruction must be drastically increased. When the American share of fishing falls off in the Atlantic, and the Pacific shore, though holding up well, excites others like Peru and Ecuador into seizing some of the successful American fishing vessels, it is not enough to suggest changes purely within the scope of current domestic and international fisheries law. Calling for a quota system, as the United States Marine Resources Council did early in 1969, may help the American fishing industry in the short run. But in longer time units it will be of insufficient help in preserving the fishery resource and in assisting the American branch of the industry.

Despite domestic and diplomatic difficulties, including both economic and political issues, the time has come to consider such things as an international fish regulatory body. Otherwise a lot of work will bring forth a legal equivalent to the sulphurated hydrocarbons that piled up the banks of the Rhine with dead fish while, presumably, leaving the water potable for the warm-blooded. Conservative thinking, combined with good intentions, cannot make a sufficiently restorative elixir.

An intensification and expansion must take place for every legal measure of practical use in protecting the environment from destructive exploitation. Beyond this there must be a coordination of these measures so that they do not exist as fragments. The coordination must be incidental to the knowledge that each of these measures has a world-wide effect. It can produce the kind of rippling consequence in nature which, up to this time, has resulted solely from the processes of exploitation. Just as no use of nature for the cash profit of urban-industrial society can take place in isolation, so no measure in-

tended for the salvation of the ecologic base of that society can occur without effecting other relationships in
the balance maintained between man and his environment. Hopefully, if the law can ever get a reversal
started in the trend toward instability that has marked
this balance since at least the eighteenth century, the
same kind of momentum can be built in the direction of
restoration as has been thrusting life forms on the earth
toward destruction.

Law, however, derives its content and purposes from
society at large. When there is enough awareness of the
need to preserve as there has been of the profit to be
earned from destroying, the law can lend its mechanisms
as thoroughly to the former as traditionally has been
done for the latter's benefit. But it is effort strengthened
by reaction between social demand and legal process.
What anesthetizes the process is satisfaction with techniques and conditions at some single point. It is necessary to realize that nature is dynamic, that even if the
present well-established trend toward destruction should
be reversed, there would never be a stationary condition
of good. Flexibility, change, a delicately tuned respon-
siveness, will always be required of law as it relates to
the environment.

To be itself honest and legitimate the law must be
made to come directly to grips with each aspect of the
current resource crisis. Only as this is done will there be
any chance at saving both technological civilization and
a favorable environment for life. The first is a convenience for man, the second a necessity.

Even if technology should shift man over to a totally
artificial basis for life, the process carrying out the
change will be legal, and the maintenance of life elements, even gases as basic as oxygen and nitrogen, will
still be essential. In the struggle for human salvation to
come the law must be exhausted as to all its possibilities
on the side of saving nature and life. The great tragedy
would be to allow legal process to work on the destructive side only. For the law, in a struggle so severe, neither neutrality nor indifference represent possibilities.

REFERENCES

Contemporary Developments in Water Law, Corwin Johnson and Susan Lewis, eds., Austin, Tex.: Center for
Research in Water Resources, 1970.

The Economics of Air Pollution: A Symposium, Harold
Wolozin, ed., New York: Norton, 1966.

Harry M. Caudill, *Night Comes to the Cumberlands: A Bi-
ography of a Depressed Area,* Boston: Little, Brown,
1963.

René Dubos, *Man Adapting,* New Haven, Conn.: Yale University Press, 1965.

Sigurd Grava, *Urban Planning Aspects of Water Pollution
Control,* New York: Columbia University Press, 1969.

Alice Harvey Hubbard, *This Land of Ours,* New York:
Macmillan, 1960.

James Willard Hurst, *Law and Social Process in United
States History,* Ann Arbor: University of Michigan Law
School, 1960.

Rodney C. Loehr, *Forests for the Future: The Story of
Sustained Yield as Told in the Diaries and Papers of
David T. Mason,* St. Paul: Minnesota Historical Society,
1952.

Erling D. Solberg, *New Laws for New Forests: Wisconsin's Forest-fire, Tax, Zoning, and County-forest Laws
in Operation,* Madison: University of Wisconsin Press,
1961.

Gilbert White, *Strategies of American Water Management,* Ann Arbor: University of Michigan Press, 1969

6

the value to man of his environment

When trying to write neutrally about values, perhaps the only way to start is with Oscar Wilde's quip about the cynic: "A man who knows the price of everything and the value of nothing." It contains a great deal of truth because there is a differentiation between worthy things expressible in cash and those that represent worth incapable of such expression. Such a distinction is not always made and very often what cannot be translated into monetary units is dismissed as either worthless or so esoteric in substance that there is no relevance to matters of material importance. In the latter case there is an equation with cash of the things of this world and an assignment of all noncash items to the realm of disembodied spirits.

Yet the value of wealth is not the only one relating to material affairs, nor are these other values of a particularly spiritual sort. For example, in the case of an individual human being, of what value is his health either to him or to society? As long as a healthful state exists it is taken as natural, as the assumption on which the matters of real consequence rest, as the way conditions ought to be. But when sickness is introduced to the organism, all the relationships change radically, with the once important world external to the single afflicted body rapidly diminishing in significance to the mind within that body.

In much of the world, production is confined to a minimum and the people held in apathy by persistent parasitic diseases. Each of these diseases may be mild and curable but not in a situation where constant reinfection occurs among an undernourished and unclean population. Under these conditions illness rather than well-being becomes the standard condition of the mass, so that planning must either divert large sums to clear up the cause of chronic sickness or else work toward norms kept low by the population's debilitated condition.

Bilharzia and yaws could probably be nearly eliminated if latrines and shoes were universally available, as well as if water used in irrigation were purified and natives turning infected soils could keep their skin covered. Merely treating the infections cannot solve the difficulty just these two diseases pose, but what would eliminate them requires a level of investment and social change not easy to carry through in the places where these diseases flourish. It is sufficient economic sustenance that is necessary to eradicate disease.

However cherished health may be when it is languishing, just how is it possible to put a value on it? The nineteenth-century medical proponents of change were not satisfied merely to build sewers, water lines, bathhouses, tenements with indoor plumbing, water filtration plants, and other means to keep free from water-borne diseases. They were also anxious to prove the dollar value of what they were doing in terms of individual human health. In somewhat grisly fashion they calculated how much a dead working-class child would have earned over a lifetime and how much illness, even when there was recovery, cost a worker who fell ill of typhoid or cholera. If all else failed, they seemed to be convinced that these tables, showing in dollars and cents what it cost to be ill and what income, taxes, and sales were lost from early death, would convert the public to a different mode of life. It was as if only a surplus cash balance, left after drawing up credits and debits for multiple lifetimes, could convince this public to make investments necessary to save life.

And how was the cash value discoverable by them? It was found in salary for days lost, payments to doctors, reduced or destroyed earning capacity, the charge of orphans cast on the guardians of the poor, and funeral expenses for plot and coffin. The value of health was reckoned in purely negative terms. By adding up these statistics, often quite problematical in terms of any hard data, their compilers hoped to show that they came to far more than the investments to prevent them. They believed their statistical methods not only convinced their opposition but actually succeeded in expressing the value they sought protection for.

It has been a method of evaluation carried over to environmental projects, for it is only reasonable to apply generally an approach man has applied to himself. The value of animals or birds or fish is often set by government agencies in terms of what hunters or fisherman spend outfitting themselves to kill such game, or what agencies spend to provide it with police protection, or what stocking or restocking some particular species has cost the taxpayers, or some combination of all three. At one time virgin land was evaluated solely in terms of the expected sales of crops grown there, without regard for whether ecologically the land would better have been left virginal. As a result, the coves and benches of Appalachia quickly lost soil richness, so that emigration had begun even before the Civil War; and the effort to settle Scandinavians on farms from upper Michigan to the Dakotas caused much resource and human suffering. Yet it has only been very lately that the employment of virginal resources—whether wildlife, grass, trees, or soil—has come to be regarded as rape rather than as procreation and profit.

Clearly, even efforts to restore something approximating the virginal condition, or to institute one meant to be as good or better, have been expressed traditionally in cash terms. The merit of soil-building often appeared in the brochures sent farmers as exclusively a matter of larger farm income. Dedicating land for game preserves is put in the guise of lower taxes and retiring land for forests as a function of subsidy or income anticipated from sales of pulp. Public projects are justified by means of savings on property losses from flooding or the expected sale of hydroelectric power. The fact flood control tends to concentrate losses both by confining a river so that only gigantic floods can reach the old flood plain and by encouraging building on that controlled plain gets played down in the estimates. So also do the side effects of stream degradation and siltation normally get passed over in the cost-benefit ratios of hydropower projects; and when they are present, they exist as figures showing what it will cost to prevent or correct them. It seems that for all this sort of work the most popular means of expression is what it costs to cure a problem, just as public health had its origin in what it costs to cure an illness.

recognizing the
need to restore balance

Admittedly, given the constant tug of war between man and his environment, between his desires and his own health, the need to restore balance is constantly present. If a man persists in overindulgence of any sort, then he had better not pretend his is a good regimen. If man organizes his demands on nature as he has been doing with ever greater efficiency since his primitive past, then he must comprehend the increasing unlikelihood of stable balances. Otherwise there must be a willingness to spend money to come to some viable balancing point between man's demands on the one side and his environment, or even his own physical limitations, on the other. The argument is not that these expenditures should not be made or calculated, but that they do not represent the value of what is acted on anymore than its ability to produce a cash return exclusively represents value. A healthy man has a value greater than his income or his medical bills, and so do the elements in his environment.

Nor can health or so human an attribute in nature as its amenity to man have its value measured by what it costs to avoid sickness. Preventive medicine, for one thing, has often come to mean mass inoculations and mass sprayings or killings against an ever broader spectrum of disease carriers in an effort to create a secure environment for man. To prevent encephalitis or malaria, lethal doses as near 100 percent effective as possible are used. To stamp out rabies, eradications of all small woodland creatures from bats to foxes are carried out. To eliminate bacteria, inoculations are carried out until zero tolerance to the diseases fought against is reached. All of this tends toward the creation of artificial regimes, whose continuance will be absolutely essential for human survival.

Increasingly, as humanly contrived protections are instituted, there are tendencies to equate these costs, including the research that led to the solutions, with the values themselves of human health and a suitable human environment. The fact is, however, that this, too, is no proper equivalency. Health is not judged by what it costs to prevent an interruption by sickness, nor is a nature perfect as a hothouse measured by the expenditures the hothouse requires—at least not until such time as man's own health and the balances in nature are utterly dependent on artificial human regimes.

cash and other measurements for value

Practically, the use of cash as a measuring device in these matters has been due to the need for some standard applicable to all values and to the popular appeal cash has as a means to measure all things. It is for these reasons that persons interested in public health and conservation strain to express risk in terms of money lost. Somehow it seems very precise to say losses to property resulting from air pollution equal $30 per person per year in the United States. This remains so, even though it is very much based on the roughest kind of guesswork and even though it ignores much of any possible larger ecologic damage. After all, if damage to buildings were the most significant consequence of polluting the air, perhaps the best solution would be to paint all structures with a self-cleansing substance that sloughs off a microscopic layer each year. This is the way that the popular, and in many ways useful, measuring tool of cash can mislead through a precision rendered spurious from an inadequate fact content; and in this, as in other cases, the probability is that it is grossly deceptive.

Other attempts at devices for the universally acceptable measurement of values in nature have been made. Calories have been suggested, as have such units of energy as the erg. The former is excellent for describing the amount of matter converted first to heat and then to energy for the production of further matter, while the latter transfers the attention normally concentrated on such numerical factors as extent of territory, distance in time, populations, incomes, expenditures, and so forth to the equally important area of energy transformation. Nearly everything is dwarfed by the expansion of energy employed in the modern urban-industrial complexes and the prospect of a sevenfold increase in thirty years makes an emphasis on energy units as a prime measuring device thoroughly reasonable.

Yet it is not probable that either of these will become the universal measuring device for describing the state of the balance between man and nature. Like cash, these units, too, do not embrace all that is to be measured, although some extension of definition can broaden their applicability. But then, this is also true of cash measurement in the hands of specialists anxious to show its scope as a universal medium. Also, neither the calorie, nor the erg, nor thermal units, nor various sorts of waves have a general currency in common speech for measuring the balance between man and his environment. This lack, however, is not an insuperable difficulty: People throughout the world have learned a wide gamut of hitherto unknown, and to them previously irrelevant, measuring units. Rather than lack of popular fashion, which might be corrected by education, it is the inability of these forms of measurement to provide a means of evaluating all things which works against them.

Then, too, it must be realized that at least up until now no inherent means of measuring value has been devel-

oped. The calorie is a unit requiring consumption to become effective as a measurer; and the erg, or other energy units, predicate conversion into energy, which for
living specimens like grass or trees or humus often
means their destruction. This is not to say the bias inherent in the function cannot be discounted: It definitely can
be, as can the bias of cash measurements once the bias
is brought up into consciousness. All it means is that
value neutrality is not yet existent even in the very devices that must be used for judging values existing or to
be created within man's environment.

Nor must any means of measuring or evaluating nature
be static. It must reflect the movement and change in nature; and in addition to being inevitably skewed to a
human frame of reference, such measurement and evaluation must incorporate rates of change occurring naturally within, or imposed by, human intervention on the
environment. For this reason the Greek planner C. A.
Doxiadis uses a unit which he calls the "human bubble."
This is what a man ideally equipped with knowledge conferred by science would perceive at any one time in any
particular spot of two meters squared in the time-space
continuum. In this system the relative, the subjective, the
transient, are fully recognized as inherent properties;
and to this are referred all other units of measurement
such as cash, calories, or ergs. Nature's subjection to
man's acts of will and humanly recognized values must
never be confused with fundamental, objective, and presumably immutable natural rules.

If this is constantly kept in mind, there can be an ec-
lectic choice of measuring and evaluating devices, because each will refer back to the penultimate judge:
man. Someday the objective means of valuation transcending beneficiaries and evaluators alike may be developed. But at the present, all value systems are flawed,
although this does not mean man is free to be arbitrary
and selfish. What keeps him from being the final judge is
the finite character of the universe compared to the
boundlessness of human aspiration. This means that failure to maintain balance between the two in routine life
must lead to disruption. Any system of measurement will

pick this up, however clouded by subjective prejudices. Today all indicators show a rapid acceleration in everything likely to produce imbalance, with every probability of a series of resource crises within the near future resulting from the final, possibly irreversible tipping of these balances.

quality and
the limits on
quantitative prediction

Quality, of course, does not tell everything needed to be known about all natural situations. It is unfortunate that numerical ordering is not a way to tell the whole story. It is for this reason that some dire predictions have not been entirely fulfilled, even though based on sound statistics. The Santa Barbara channel oil seepage did not prove as destructive to life structures as predicted. A readjustment was made more quickly than anyone could have expected. Life forces often show a greater or a lesser resiliency to catastrophe than quantitative studies indicate; and while this can be a base for neither optimism nor pessimism, it must be a cause for modesty in all predictions of the response to change by natural phenomena based on numerical calculations.

It is possible perfect knowledge of natural forces might be numerically expressed; but not only is this currently impossible, it may never be so in the case of trace minerals or minute aspects of some life forces. Assuredly, pending such certainty, the leap over ignorance, jumping from one known fact to another, will continue to remain a part of every predictive or prescriptive human act concerning the environment. Nor as long as humility is kept a part of the process, need this be anything more than another of the several risks incident to the experience of living. Only when insistence is made that such regions of ignorance do not exist, or shall very soon utterly disappear, do the risks become perilous.

Of course, none of this can be a guise for avoiding discovery of data, along with its rapid assimilation into a coordinated course of decision-making. A far greater accuracy can be attained in describing the costs and benefits of everything man does than what has been made available up to this time. Such data make possible a degree of specificity in allocating costs not previously feasible and converts to existing political realities what would have been an impossible mode of behavior.

In this last regard one cannot overlook the role of capital formation and the function its sheer size plays in comparison with the work the capital is expected to perform. In this sense it is ironic that only by processing his environment through his economic enterprises can man acquire the means to preserve from himself nature's essential character, which is its viability. Knowledge is an essential factor in securing the release of money, or labor, or material resources, or energy from a nation's accumulated capital; and the more specifically the costs and benefits are stated to man as a living creature, to man as an economic being, and to the environment man possesses, the more difficult is resistance rendered to this purpose.

The plea, so often made in nineteenth-century Europe and America, that scarce capital earned the largest dividends in commercial and industrial enterprise was not to be lightly dismissed. It is the same argument made today in developing countries pressed to make investments for economic growth or in advanced economies where the competition for capital has grown so keen that resource protection loses to more cash-earning investments. It was this kind of opposition, seemingly so pragmatic, which drove the nineteenth-century public health reformers to calculate the value in cash of the losses suffered from sickness and death. This same tactic forces the proponent of natural protection to calculations of costs and benefits of the most specific sort in order to show who is getting precisely what from where at the cost of whom in the mutual process of acquisition and deprivation.

Only in resource use specificity can the proof be offered as to what the total charges will be. In this task, quantitative language and the solid data on which it rests have a large role to play. Their substantial lack of existence in the nineteenth century acted both to drive scientists toward formulating the discipline of statistics and as a clog on needed change. Inescapably, the political arena is the point at which values come to either conflict or peaceful resolution; and in their coming together for short-range personal or group or regional advantage values can be made to shine as brightly as those of long-range, even universal worth. Nothing speaks for itself in the polemics of politics, for, as has been said, a tree cannot fight back. The ecologic interest must have its spokesmen; and they must do the fighting for the trees —or species of more argumentative worth, like snakes, insects, hyenas, and others generally lacking existing appeal for man.

Intuition and emotion are not enough in the work of environmental regulation. Indeed, in the case of snakes, insects, and hyenas the emotional reaction may be entirely for their quick destruction. Only by way of a quantitatively measured, rational argument made on their behalf as integral parts of biological control systems can man be convinced he must not impose the lethal dose of a 100 percent kill on them. The solid marshaling of facts may pry loose the sort of investment so consistently refused until the present century. Truly, as such evidence has been accumulated and brought forward as proof, each decade of the twentieth century has seen greater investment from the capital stocks of money, energy, labor, and physical material go into the protection of the environment; and it has been an investment accelerating its growth rate several times each decade, so that what seemed a major contribution in the administration of Theodore Roosevelt looked modest by 1970. In this way the efforts at building up the hard data and of putting arguments in the concrete terms of who gets what at whose expense have paid off. Definitely, given the success such a technique has had, it will remain of prime importance in the future.

But the importance is prime and not exclusive of all other values, purposes, or techniques for their translation into reality. Even in matters of purely economic choice, quantitative methods cannot make the final judgment by themselves. The decision will not be a self-made one but will require the introduction of something else to produce the decisive order.

For example, in the state of Washington rain makers can bring down rain almost on command; but if they precipitate it when the wheat growers want moisture, the cherry crop will be forestalled. The options are several. The first would make the rainfall, benefiting the cherry industry there more than it would the wheat. The second would bring down the rain, profiting the wheat industry at the expense of the cherry. The third would ask biologists to develop new strains of both cherry and wheat, with synchronized growth demands. And the fourth would abandon one or both, so that more manageable crops could be introduced into what has become an artificial regime of biological maintenance. Even economics, the most measurable of disciplines, and climatology, a science based on physical data, can be so influenced by biological phenomena that within these quantitative systems they must deny the decision maker a completely numerical answer.

*the decision
to maintain wilderness*

The task of determining whether to preserve a wilderness cannot be easy. This is something quite different from determining whether to maintain either parks or tree farms, which are what recycled forests are, yet it is not easy to get some persons to grasp that difference. Park managers judge the success of their parks by the amount of human use each receives; and commercial forest managers evaluate their operations in terms of the size and speed of income returned following each reforestation.

Beginning with grants from John D. Rockefeller, Jr., the National Park Service has built hard-surfaced roads into many previously wild regions. Hotels, campsites, restaurants, and other devices to lure people into entering the parks have been built, with the result that since 1917 the Park Service can show a steep increase in people using the parks. And as for the commercial forests, they, too, are similarly humanly busy places where undergrowth is cut out as a fire hazard, parasites are removed as competitors for growth foods, and whole regions are kept artificially in a stage of species succession at some point short of the natural climax.

For these reasons although parks and forest may be far from metropolitan regions, with a slight permanent population, they are integrally a part of urban-industrial civilization. This is true as to their manner of use, the source of the investments for their support, and the roles they are expected to play in the future; and the result has been some very heavy demands in purely physical terms. In the case of the more popular parks, demand is such that in order to maintain a minimally desirable condition within them the number allowed entry each year may have to be limited. While as for the commercial forest, it may someday take on about as natural an appearance to even the untrained city eye as a coffee plantation or a shady grove at the church picnicking grounds.

What is unfortunate is not necessarily that this should describe most parks and forests, but that so many of their managers find it hard to conceive of any alternative and, consequently, cannot see the reasons for protecting existing wilderness from conversion into just these sort of parks and forests. Indeed, some forest managers act as if the forest could not exist without their assistance, and as if, with commercial management, all of a forest's survival problems disappear. The ideal is held up of a forest with competitors for the trees' nutrition cleared away, with combustible undergrowth gone, and with trees culled out whose numbers would hold back growth of the better specimens. Prominent in this purpose are ideas interpreting parts of the forest's natural growth as excessive and as a pest to the rest, which thereby has assigned it implictly a higher order or value. It is, indeed, a positive value to the other negative ones, so far as the health of a forest is to be determined under such a view's control; but it is a value system peculiarly human, for it imposes on the vegetation purposes external to the basic one of growth. To grow and to survive through the growth process represent the natural purpose of each plant, regardless of its effect on others or even on itself. Anything else is a human contrivance to fulfill a humanly conceived purpose.

the reasons for human
interposition throughout nature

In itself there is nothing to be condemned in human intervention. If any part of the balance between man and his environment is to be maintained, there will have to be an interlocking, world-wide system of artificial regimes. Many humanly understood ecologic goals require such actions. Deer, for example, require a certain kind of forest, and if forest in a wide region is allowed to go on to its natural climax, deer will be shut out. The types of woods most desirable to the paper and plywood industry are this kind of wood; and they can be cut young for industrial use. Therefore, the rapidly recycled forest is congenial to deer, so that this purpose requires active intervention to keep up a deer population in areas distant from agriculture.

Unstable forest conditions, existing somewhere short of their natural climax, are often most valuable commercially; nor can one overlook the cutting of forests at delicate ecologic turning points in a region. In the latter case, in order to prevent nature from grooving an irreversible course, human interposition must reconstitute a forest that might disappear in the natural sequence of events. Treating human interposition as an inherently wicked abuse of nature is as moralistic and deficient a view as one that never sees merit in the way nature shifts for itself without human help.

Those who see forests as being best off when most protected from the challenge of natural growth overlook the fact that their acts often expose the forests to other risks that will require a deeper human effort. When species in a forest are reduced to one, that forest is more vulnerable to disease than a multispecies forest; and when the single type is highly resinous, fire becomes a great menace. When undergrowth is too sharply cut away, the soil can erode even in a forest and, in any case, the rebuilding of soil is slowed or stopped. Animal types also go down drastically and, because food must be scarce in such a forest, so do absolute numbers, except for those creatures that find the single favored species of tree a favorable food source. In that event an otherwise innocuous animal becomes converted into a menace to an entire forest. Before dangers such as these the variousness of the naturally growing forests have higher resistances and are less threatened with total destruction. Clearly, therefore, all risks are not concentrated in a natural forest left as nearly as possible to its own internal, nonhumanly determined rules.

Still, it is not a choice solely between artificial and natural regimes. With but a few exceptions, even commercially recycled forests depend heavily on natural processes and allow considerable unregulated natural behavior to the forest. Neither the economic means nor the economic motive are present to stimulate a different attitude. Nor can all forests not suited for recycling function best without extensive human intervention, insofar as their protection of soil from erosion, streams from siltation, or game from extinction is concerned. Much land is too steep or unstable to allow trees to be planted, cut, planted, cut, and so on in endless sequence. The commercial forest, able to pay its own costs of maintenance, is not a model capable of universal application, nor are such uncuttable forests always suitable for alternative park use. They may be remote, lacking the means for economically having communication provided them, too precipitous for camping, or impractical for general recreational use for some other reason.

It is simply a fact that there are forests not usable for lumbering or parks, which must still be maintained through heavy investments of money and labor if other ecologic values are to be kept up, ranging all the way from small game to possibly even climate. As for climate being affected by forests, extravagant claims have been made, but modest experiments indicate a much slighter relationship for rainfall, depth of temperature, and general humidity. But even by the modest tests, forests useless for lumbering and of small utility for recreation have had an apparently good effect on keeping up rainfall and humidity as well as holding precipitation in the ground after it has reached the earth. Yet even should these prove a minor gain, in the lack of a better purpose the benefits of such noncyclable forests are sufficient to justify planting and preserving them.

And more important, not only is there unlikely to be any better purpose, but the probabilities are that purely negative consequences will be the alternative. The sharper slopes, the thinner soils, the watersheds of rivers with heavy sediment levels, should have as heavy a mat of vegetation over them as can be kept growing, and when game needs sanctuary, woods having no other function must be kept available. Any other attitude is to have substituted not an economic for an ecologic point of view, but a very partial economic outlook.

the difficulty of
preserving wilderness

In a world dominated by man it is hard to see even the preservation of primal conditions as free of human values. It is well proved that even unto the Antarctic the world is interjected with the chlorinated hydrocarbons, and the patterns of bird migrations have been so broken up that often life systems far from direct human contact have been deeply affected. Consequently, it is just not possible to talk of setting up zones into which man cannot reach. The world is a single system, basically a closed one despite extensions like aerospace explorations, and what is done in one part affects many other parts in one degree or another, either physically or biologically. At the best, only a partially effective quarantine is an available choice, with many dangerous penetrations into the protected areas, as happens in even the best-run quarantine programs.

And as for values, even if wilderness should be kept here and there, the primary moving factor will be economic. There may be a further ecologic argument, but when people speak of holding moisture in the soil, barring the slippage of hillsides, stopping erosion, covering streams from siltation, keeping up plant cross-fertilization by providing provender for bees and butterflies, or whatever the "natural" argument put forward, a direct economic benefit normally is to be perceived. Nothing, for example, could encourage the Mediterranean countries to allow conditions to recur that would permit the return of malaria. The ecologic side effects of chemical pesticides mean very little weighed beside the threat of malaria's return.

Genuine ecologic values can mask economic ones, and the same is true for those of an educational or aesthetic character. In fact, disentangling each from the other is hard enough in any event, but trying to drain them of all economic significance is nearly an impossibility. Trying to act on motives purely of an ecologic, educational, or esthetic kind is on a par with efforts to so behave in economics as to avoid ecologic, educational, or aesthetic effects. Not only is the world one closed system, of which man is a part despite his will and his aspiration, but all of man's means of evaluating his place in things interlace so as themselves to compose a unity.

Whatever the intentions or the distinctions insisted on by man, his impact on the environment has a unity of effect. Scarcely can one of these objects be carried out than it helps or impedes the others. The gravest lack is not suppressing one or more, but in bringing them into a stable balance. So frustrated have those become who have concern for the environment that they damn economics or engineering or technology and call for their discard. Putting aside the political changes of such a program, it is quite doubtful if ecologic or other values ultimately would be served. Investments are needed to protect the balance nature has with man and it is out of man's economic activity that those investments will come. Suppression of any value always seems the easier course, but in the longer run it will be a mutual, reciprocating development dictated by multiple purposes that will determine the future relations between man and his environment.

the effect of future
large populations on nature

Economic factors and man's technical skills, however, cannot be allowed to dominate quite to the degree common since the eighteenth century. Burgeoning population, with its increased spending power and growing gross national product, has been desirable for economic and political reasons throughout man's history; and a purely economic valuation would keep the old premium on such growth through the next century and a quarter. On this calculation, with the world's human population now doubling itself every thirty years, by about A.D. 2100, a humanity of 50 billion people would exist, fed on synthesized food, maintained at leisure in an artificial environment compacted by crowding. The famines some predict from population growth before 1980 are dismissed as technologically unlikely or else as transitory in effect.

In such a scheme of things man would almost entirely cease to function as a sensate being and, as a mass, have to find his satisfaction from the invisible, hence infinite, world of the intellect. Activity, aggression, speed, silence, solitude, risk, personal sensate experience of great variety, would be reserved for those engaged in space travel and colonization, the maintenance of which would be a substantial part of the earth's reasons for economic activity. On the world itself the highest value would be on the sedentary. Action, violence, would be out of place. Lapped in a molded armchair, fed synthetic foods, enveloped in an artificial environment, supported by computerized industry, surrounded by sources of information, totally free for intellectual play and idle dreaming, economics and technology would have re-created Eden for the single world-city of an urban-industrial mankind.

A vision like this is no prophecy, for it is not inevitable. Enormous effort and risk must go into constructing such a paradise; and if it succeeds, whether by 2100 or later, much investment and fortunate combination of circumstance must occur. In short, to bring about a New Jerusalem of this kind, careful planning, work, and luck in about equal measure will be needed. The fact that man may be started upon a course does not mean he will successfully complete it. The present increase in population, its movement to the cities, the cities' sprawl over the countryside, the processing of nature, the involvement of man in experience mostly through television, the rise of the drug culture, and the casting away of tradition may be the evidence of such a future; but these still lie in a present where change, perhaps by catastrophe, is possible. What supports this prospect is still a very delicate, chancy mechanism that can be dislocated or broken in preference for something else or for oblivion.

Clearly, if this is man's chosen goal, all talk of preserving wild land, wildlife, or variety in life species is futile. Space, highly valuable economically in a crowded world which technology could sustain, simply will not be available for much openness. What is needed is to determine if this is the future that is wanted by man in terms of its suitability for himself or its attainability related to his character.

For the first time man can order his future environment and his future state within it as in the past he could order his clothing or his shelter. The environment has become a larger shelter for his occupation; and his freedom, though not complete, is very large in how he orders each aspect of his life. Simply, he must ask himself if open space, low levels of human density, movement, physical action, and direct sensate experience are important to him.

A life without these would not be physically healthful; but that has never been a deterrence to man's desires. Besides, adjustments in diet, drugs, the provision of mechanically manipulative therapy, could counteract the effects of inactivity and already are doing so for millions of urban dwellers. It is really in the area of man's will and imagination that these questions must be answered. He has broken nature's resistance and he can bring his own body around to what he wants for it, although both come with great sacrifice. The unresolved issue is whether he can fit his own psychology to such a future and, if he could, whether he should want to do it.

Definitely there are dire prophets. Some claim man has innate impulses to violence which cannot be curbed or always channeled. Others argue man cannot abide noise levels above certain strengths without permanent harm and that he has a limit of how many neighbors he can take without individual impairment. In the 1950s Robert Lindner foresaw a sharp rise in crime from spiraling numbers of sociopaths whose superego controls present culture had kept from forming, while in the 1960s Paul Goodman called for a crash program to get at least 20 percent out of the jammed slums and into open country so that some might be salvaged from the harm of crowded, shapeless conditions.

Yet there is no proof that these statements have any truth in them at all. Perhaps, as a garrulous animal, man likes overcrowding. Harmed or not, the young prefer music at its loudest; and they shrug off the experiments that put down this preference. Surveys show man is upset only by unexpected noise and seems unaware of invariably high decibel ratings. Crime and sociopathy are rising, but in a tightly controlled future environment external restraints might reduce this activity to very low levels.

In short there are none to tell today's generations what they can or cannot do, any more than there is any way to write a policy to insure some particular kind of future. Extending present lines of growth into an indefinite future to do so is unsatisfactory; intuiting breaks in those lines are as often wrong as they are right; and planning on a statistical basis serves as no more than a combination of these methods. Whoever talks about the future for man is no better than his information, perception, intelligence, and above all, luck that man will behave as he foresaw.

man's future
freedom of choice

Man has great freedom of choice, and unless he is constitutionally limited by some inherent death urge, he should be shaping the future as he chooses. Otherwise, as the legal historian William Hurst would put it, the powerful forces of apathy and drift may create for him something both unbearable and irreversible. If such is allowed to happen, given the powers even now available to man, the consequence will seem more stupid than tragic. Though every generation has always been a transitional one and important to the development of human culture, the generations functioning between now and the year 2000 have greater responsibilities than most have had and on their choice of values depends the future of man and nature. Henceforward, though man must live with his power to destroy all life, he is not bound to the inevitabilities inhibiting the predecessor generations.

It should also be realized that any decision taken will require several years to show the slightest effect on established trends. Far from revealing immediately dramatic results, it would take between twenty and thirty years to produce not a total change but rather a substantial difference in the way things are done. It is not only a forest that requires time to grow but also altered human institutions. In order to land a man on the moon in 1969, which was largely just a technological feat, a crash program for twelve preceding years had been required which built, in turn, upon work done at more leisurely pace over the preceding three decades. Certainly when social, economic, and political changes as well must be made, the time needed for change can be of no less duration. If those are right who tell the world there cannot be the luxury of time but that the basic problems must be solved within the next five years, then mankind is doomed.

Within five years man needs to decide the world he wants in 2000 and the trends he believes should be established to get the world safely to some sort of balance by 2100. He cannot afford himself the luxury of leaving all to chance or to millennia of slow change. Definitely, though, he cannot remake the world in that brief length of time. Efforts to do so would more likely lead, not to constructive change, but to resistances that would produce paralysis or destruction. And at this juncture, it would be very dangerous to precipitate either, for one or the other would condemn future generations to extinction or intense suffering.

The four generations now alive have a sort of collective power to choose, not just for themselves but for many future generations, the values on which earthly life will rest. Definitely, when the choices are made, they ought to be done cleanly, honestly, intelligently, and with a sense of the responsibility involved. Anything less is reminiscent of the behavior of Sodom and Gomorrah during the visit of Lot's angels, and the consequences would be far more deserved.

What must be done cannot be completed in the lifetime of even the youngest now alive, but it can be begun so that the first small results could appear before the death of those among the eldest. If nothing is done to make these constructive choices, then so fast are the trends now in progress moving, that people currently past forty can expect to see the resulting catastrophe. The twentieth century has had a way of telescoping events in time because of the forces technology has released.

In choosing the essential values for emphasis and selecting others for playing down, guidance is hard to find. Perhaps the most constant touchstone is the idea of balance between man and his environment. Certainly it would seem wise not to destroy any existing ecumene in nature until man knows the full scope of its operation and has at hand the artificial regime that will replace the function of what he is knocking out. At the same time, he should have some order of priorities so that he does not institute an artificial regime requiring enormous investments to replace a natural life system operating with minimal input of energy. Until the knowledge is available to move with confidence along these lines, the better course is a constant caution that explores existing balances, even as adjustments are being made for richer human living.

Before liquidating any life form, man should find out three facts. First, he must inquire if he is truly eliminating it or only converting it to something more troublesome than what prompted his initial concern. Second, he must discover the effect the successful liquidation will have on other organisms connected in an interlocking ecumene, so that he may make up in some other way the now missing element. And third, he must ask if what he is doing is worth carrying out the more elaborate way or whether some more modest adjustment might not do just as well. Only when he feels fairly secure in answering these queries should man move firmly ahead.

The day is past when the world could bear man's blithely clearing continents of forest cover, eliminating masses of species, discharging gases into the air, washing soil from entire mountain ranges into the sea, or doing any of the previously common employments of nature. So delicate has the balance become that chemical pesticide programs, up to this point slighter in effect than any of these, seemingly cannot be borne by an afflicted nature despite its real value for human health, amenity, and economic growth. Definitely, here is something that in its earliest stages showed its impact on nature and nature's apparent inability to bear up under the blow. Because it now stands neither alone nor can be called the most dangerous, it clearly reveals that the balance between man and nature is threatened as never before in the course of mankind's development. Therefore, putting the current emphasis on the value of this balance as the guideline for future behavior seems fully appropriate.

Of course, knowledge of and control over nature will soon advance to the point where men can substitute fully artificial regimes to regulate the entirety of human and natural functions. When that happens, the world will have become a garden of preselected life forms. Human population and conduct will have stabilized along patterns determined solely by the purposes programmed into the regime. However, such knowledge presently seems lacking that would create artificial regimes capable of fully realizing human potential and keeping alive in the garden of the earth a large variety of life forms. Only very limiting regimes of this kind could be set up on the basis of what is presently known. But soon or late, until the total knowledge exists for such all-encompassing artificiality, the highest value for man is the viable balance between himself and the nature that composes his environment.

As the physicist John Rader Platt has said, the era of

natural selection, after 3 billion years, is at an end. Now it is the age of human selection operating by way of pollution, predation, and deliberate alterations. The selections may occur through accident, mistake, or chosen design, but the process by which the selection is currently and henceforward made will be as a result of human in lieu of natural acts. Given a world so based on human behavior, the least to be demanded of man is a purpose toward his environment transcending nature's exploitation and eventual destruction as a living, renewing force. If this minimum, complex though it is, cannot be met, then everything else is as conversations among the terminally ill: preparations for, or dodges from, approaching death.

REFERENCES

Environments of Man, Jack B. Bresler, ed., Reading, Mass.: Addison-Wesley, 1968.

Joint House-Senate Colloquium to Discuss a National Policy for the Environment, July 17, 1968, 90th Cong., 2nd Sess., Print No. 8 for the Senate Committee on Interior and Insular Affairs and the House Committee on Science and Technology.

Allan G. Bogue, *From Prairie to Cornbelt: Farming on the Illinois and Iowa Prairies in the 19th Century,* Chicago: Quadrangle Books, 1968.

Fred Cottrell, *Energy and Society: The Relation Between Energy, Social Change, and Economic Development,* New York: McGraw-Hill, 1955.

Constantinos A. Doxiadis, *Ekistics: An Introduction to the Science of Human Settlements,* New York: Oxford University Press, 1968.

D. S. Halacy, Jr., *The Weather Changers,* New York: Harper & Row, 1968.

John V. Krutilla, *The Columbia River Treaty, The Economics of an International River Basin Development,* Baltimore: Johns Hopkins, 1967.

Seymour Melman, *Our Depleted Society,* New York: Holt, Rinehart and Winston, 1965.

7

the time limits for man's future

the worsening crisis in man's environment

Throughout the world there exists an accelerating crisis between man and his environment. Partly the crisis is merely cumulative. Settled agricultural life is not over ten thousand years old, but from its beginning, the demands made on soil and vegetation have tended to be exhausting. It has been an area of exhaustion extended more and more widely throughout the world as man shifted to permanent agricultural settlements, thereby increasing both his number and his pressure on resources. Millennia have passed with an unremitting stepping up of these consequences, and as a result, at least part of today's problem is a cultural inheritance from at least neolithic times.

The crisis is multiplied, however, by the growth of a world-encompassing urban-industrial culture. What previously had been regional became global; what previously had been confined to agriculture as despoliation was enormously extended by the growth in urban need. Poor as earlier traditions may have been relating man to his environment, they collapsed even as ideals under the impact of this change in man's life.

Previously, strong forces pushed toward static conditions; and though certainly not meant for this purpose, they often had operated as protectors of the environment. But the one dominant fact in urban-industrial culture has been its dynamic quality, its attraction toward change, and its fatal effect on any tradition favoring the static. In a world where increases in population, energy, expectations, have been explosive in their growth, the result scarcely could fail to penetrate the most remote parts of the world.

Despite everything experienced up to this point, currently young adults living to middle age can expect to see an investment in urban growth two and one-half times the total made by man from his emergence as a species down to the present. There will simultaneously be a far greater increase in relative production of energy, particularly if a commercial nuclear fusion process for energy production should be discovered. Even if one were rather critical of the precision of such predictions, those ecologists concerned with the present impact of material production and energy demand levels have reason to feel besieged. At a time when both seem at the point of beginning an unprecedented trajectory upward, they are concerned with what has already happened to the environment.

Naturally, this puts them at the sharpest of odds with most of the planners for the future who foresee no other way than to increase energy levels, networks of transportation, and material productivity. The curve of rising human expectations demands them. These demandants are not interested in being told by ecologists that man should cut back rather than increase his energy demands, level off his productivity, and seek to discover the minimum he needs to sustain a comfortable and secure existence. This attitude insists that it is man's role to push ahead to ever higher levels of amenity rather than accept some lower common denominator for the conditions of his life. For many ecologists this ignores the limitations inherent in the living world of nature which exist apart from the ever-growing ability to exploit these limited resources.

the
suspicions of technology

It is an argument far from resolution and the facts that could resolve it are not known. Certainly it is a dangerous position to take which sees any limit on technology's ability to handle future problems of natural supply in relation to human demand. So many who would have played Cassandra have been proven wrong by events, that anyone seeing constraints in nature not technically or economically surmountable is viewed with the sharpest suspicion. So successful has technology shown itself to be under these challenges that now the contrary is being insisted on, namely that neither nonrenewable resources nor those renewable by natural process will ever be exhausted by human demand. In this view, given sufficient provocation, man will always manage to desalinate the oceans or wring moisture from the atmosphere to meet any demand he might have for water, while as for air, he could always manage its purification by washing all impurities from it.

Yet should this all prove true, there is more to the relationships in nature than the availability of particular elements, particularly such chemical ones as compose air and water. In the late nineteenth century some materialists were very gleeful in that it took less than a dollar's worth of certain chemicals to make a man; and the novelist Theodore Dreiser seized on this to assert that man was no more than "physico-chemisms." Some considerable accumulation of knowledge has been obtained in the decades since, and while chemistry and biology have unities, they are not so simple as mixing a few powders to make life. This is not to play down the importance of chemistry in, say, water pollution, where the toughest culprit in dispute has not yet been elected between phosphate, nitrate, and trace minerals. But it is to say that water without living organisms has very little meaning to a man who cares about the relations between life and its backing. There are a few allotrophic lakes almost purely H_2O, and their utter quietude must convince anyone that there is more to maintaining the environment than making distilled water from the ocean or refining it from the atmosphere. In their own way, lakes of such a purity have an eeriness equal to those emptied of life by acid or oxygen exhaustion.

To some the difficulty is not the inability of man's technology to maintain for his economy enough individual stock and flow resources so as to bar the exhaustion of any one of them. Fear of resource exhaustion has been common to one or another conservationist. It may well be, however, that improved technology has removed the basis of these fears. But what remains as yet unproven is whether the system interlocking physical and life forms throughout the world is salvageable through a few technical adjustments or whether more basic changes between nature and urban-industrial society are required.

Beginning in the nineteenth century, as the release of energy hit exponential rates of increase, both income and material demands began a similar vertical rise. One of the results has been that even as world population has risen as never before, the densities began dropping about a century ago below previously long-established levels. The meaning of this is that man spilled out over the earth like quicksilver from a broken thermometer, except that man keeps up an increasing stream of human numbers, demands for space and for everything contained within that space.

Technology has been the expediter of demand rather than the limiting agent, and the current question is whether the total life system can withstand pressure of such present and, more significantly, prospective magnitudes without a collapse. It is not, therefore, the peril to individual resources that is important. Instead, it is the risks being imposed on the universal biological order.

political responses for environmental protection

Already tremors are beginning to produce legal consequences in the political structures. Some states have banned the best known of the chlorinated hydrocarbons, DDT. Substantial grants are being made by agencies of the United States government allowing a substitution of biological for chemical control of the environment. The California Senate wants to outlaw the gasoline engine for automobiles by 1975. The United States required as of 1970 that ecologic considerations be given every enterprise supported by the federal government on the model of the Full Employment Act of 1946. Nor has this been confined only to the United States. However, with certain exceptions, especially the United Kingdom and Scandinavia, American lawmakers have probably pushed further along this line than those in other countries, if for no other reason than that the problems in the United States are older, more advanced, and on a larger scale than elsewhere. It may be that the dangers are simply more to be apprehended where the harm is greatest.

Several years ago the economist and then German chancellor Ludwig Erhard said that the next major political question for mankind was the maintenance of an ecologic base capable both of supporting man in comfort and maintaining its own stability. Because this has not appeared to the past as a matter of much, if any, significance, there exist few legal institutions for carrying out such a program. It is true there has been a concern beginning in the eighteenth century. Slowly through the nineteenth century this produced sewerage and health boards at the local level, national ministries of health on the continent and abortive efforts for them in England and the United States, reforestation beginning in southeastern France under Napoleon I, a theory for a national natural resource policy put forward by some Italian legal theorists in the early nineteenth century, and in the United States after the Civil War state agencies for health, fisheries, forests, and parks.

Historically, interest in the environment has concentrated in Europe and America in three periods: just before World War I, during the depression of the 1930s as largely a make-work effort, and since 1960. In Russia it came, after some interest in reforestation by Tsar Alexander I, with the development of soil science in the Ukraine under Alexander III and again since 1960, but on a far broader scale. China has had considerable attention paid her natural resources by the present govern-

138

*man
and his
environment:
law*

ment, though, as in the sparrow destruction campaign, some of it has intensified the tradition of steady extirpation of surviving species. The interest in the environment by different countries in the past cannot be put on a calendar of simultaneous dates, though interest has risen and fallen in many of them from Japan, through the Balkans, to Latin America, as any comparative study would show.

What is new since 1960 has been the appearance of a simultaneous world-wide interest in the ecology. Its strength has varied only in terms of the strength of the different economies and the degree to which their cultures have the capacity to deal with such challenges. In even remote places the interest has risen, and it can only be explained by a vague but universal perception of the rising danger of failure to deal with the growing imbalance between man and his environment.

In a world where technological change is so rapid that some blithe spirits are making schematic drawings for lunar cities by 2000, it is very easy to forget that changes of an institutional sort—social, economic, political, and legal—do not move so rapidly even though their rate of alteration also has sharply increased. Should the most extravagant predictions of technical progress prove both swift and accurate, they still must come from this planet's resources and make the bulk of their effect felt here upon this earth. Furthermore, as a practical matter, many of the present projections will have their greatest impact in the twenty-first century; and already it is by no means too soon to consider projections, not for 2000, but for 2100. But even as this is done, it ought not be forgotten that the present century has a full generation left in it, which not only must be shuffled through but in which crucial decisions must be made. Too concentrated an attention on the plane for lunar cities might be a very risky diversion at this stage of environmental conditions.

The more realistic, if less romantic, course of action might be that of politicians who also serve as spokesmen for industries in such fields as space exploration, national security, air travel, and electronics—all of which seem to be the interlocked base for the computer future.

Now many of them simultaneously are pushing legislation that will require a firm national ecologic policy and federal agencies to protect the total environment. They mean to open further avenues through which could move the demands and counterdemands that have been building up over the past several generations. Already under existing legal structures improved regulations have been issued, such as those relating to oil exploitation in federally controlled areas by the United States Department of the Interior.

The American political establishment believes production is of the greatest importance. Nevertheless it has been required by the circumstances of a severely disturbed environment to issue orders putting on much severer limits than most would have anticipated. Even those who see the environment essentially in terms of service material for the human economy or, more narrowly, of the national interest begin to perceive the vital need to preserve nature if for no other reason than that it is such a source.

*the current
popularity for
resource protection*

Certainly it is encouraging when political leaders from differing parties usually thought of as "realistic" are moved to push for the legal importance of ecologic considerations. It is a long step forward from the bitter opposition President Benjamin Harrison met with when he created the first national forests or the sort of protection natural resources received under the administration of someone like President Warren Harding. More important, there is support at the popular level today of an intensity and depth simply not present in the past.

When Thomas Jefferson instructed the expedition to the Louisiana Purchase to survey its natural resources, popular opinion treated those instructions as commands to disclose the riches to be expected by new settlements. Within a generation the beaver were gone; within three generations, the buffalo; in four generations, the native perennial grasses; and five generations later saw the soil itself blowing away. Only then, when it had become evident the country's center could not support the weight of economic activity possible to the three coasts and the Great Lakes, were some of the restrictions in Jefferson's instructions recalled and a later President, Franklin Roosevelt, able to set up conservation programs for the area.

Necessity is more often the source of widespread support than sensitive anticipation of events, though it may come a bit late for maximum effectiveness or, sometimes, for sufficiency itself. But when a needed change comes, it is not to be despised for being rather late or having fairly crass motivations. The far more significant issue today for the popular policy of politicians who want to protect nature mainly for human exploitation is whether their basic assumption is tenable, which calls for the simultaneous maximization of human productivity and the optimization of the conditions of man's environment.

Lord Molson, chairman of the Council for the Preservation of Rural England, has asked if it is possible to combine certain extractive businesses, which leave land derelict, with expanding populations and steadily rising demands for land space. These are conflicting human demands, with a sort of substratum of biological content, which may be severe enough. Still, taxing as they are, they could be met by either greater restoration efforts or by cutting back the expectations for greater land space. Not even Lord Molson sees looming any larger conflict nor assumes the possibility of more drastic action.

Yet the chance for both is present. In a planet of circumscribed resources dominated by economic man with his escalating productivity, his unlimited aspirations for personal material betterment, his expansion of energy requirements on an open-ended pattern, and his decision to explore both the universe and other galaxies out of the accumulated means of this planet, the question must be asked if the earth has a sufficient inventory for doing it all.

Nor is the problem eased by the human tradition of

wars and preparations for wars which, as technology has improved, have put ever greater tasks upon the world's resources. Even as humanity has vigorously pursued the materially demanding aspects of its intellect in fields ranging from home television to the likelihood of looping Jupiter, the apparent irrationalities of class, caste, tribe, religion, race, nation, and ideology have shown indications of intensifying rather than lessening, so that the drafts upon nature increase rather than dimish. Being man-centered, humanity has regretted these conflicts in terms of losses to human life and investment; but if the sights were raised a little higher, man might see that, even on terms of his own best interest, it is now less these potential losses that ultimately matter than the harm thrust upon the reviving powers of his environment.

Yet exorbitant as are the prospective demands of war and the present requirements of preparation for it, the potentially more massive needs come from the rapidly expanding, apparently limitless demands of urban-industrial society when it is at its peaceful, thriving tasks. Without slanting the answer one way or the other, it is absolutely necessary to ask whether or not the existence of such an economy shall forever be compatible with the viability of an environment sustaining itself by processes of natural renewal. Definitely what ought not to be merely assumed is their ability to exist side by side if only man is careful of the strength and weaknesses of the ecology. A more profound choice than this may be essential.

*the chances
for compatibility
between man and nature*

Of course this is not to say careful management cannot keep up for a long time a balance of the two under quite adverse conditions, as some reforestation projects show. Many, observing craggy mountains bare of trees, are prone to insist that since they had never grown there in a state of nature, trying to plant them would be unnatural and useless, like the Russians' effort to afforest the Aleutians in 1805. Though there are places to which trees were unknown except in stunted variants of larger species, persistence often shows forestry possible where none would have predicted success.

In 1937 the Irish government planted a forest in the Shehy mountains near the shrine of Gougane Barra at the source of the river Lee. Prints from the eighteenth century showed the slopes completely bare of trees, with forbidding rock outcroppings over their surfaces. Evergreen seedlings were set out, nevertheless, for forests far up these slopes, and a generation later trees are flourishing where the eighteenth-century print would have deemed it impossible. Not even the severe erosion following the original cutting had prevented some return of the trees. Already the foresters are cutting trees for palings and rustic housing decoration and talk is heard of a paper industry in the neighborhood in the future.

And it is just here that the questioning observer is brought most abruptly back to the issue of whether the demands of urban-industrial society and the limits of the natural ecology are compatible, even when some human assistance goes to the latter. Clearly in the Gougane Barra forest evergreen growth is not the climax tree, and if the forest is allowed to fulfill its sere, it will go on to deciduous trees on the gentler slopes. Only effort by foresters can keep it at the present stage. Furthermore, it is doubtful if any tree lacking a grasping, fairly shallow root system, able to derive much of its water from surface runoff, could grow anywhere except in Green Valley Desmond, the only fairly level ground in the forest. In addition, lumbering outside of that valley would only reproduce the stark conditions of the eighteenth-century print, with a poorer chance of again reversing it. This is not to say a paper industry could not develop in County Cork, but it is to say it would require the use of valley floors for forestation rather than the dramatically reclothed slopes. Given the rapid growth of Cork City and the popularity of Gougane Barra to visitors, the sole use of such woods for recreation might be far more economic and ecologically practicable, or else man as an economist ought to realize such tracts are simply best situated when allowed an undisturbed tree cover. Those who view such areas as places for recycled forests meant to supply pulp to the paper industry are seeing something without the capacity for survival. The compatibility just does not exist between uses of this intense a sort and a viable, self-renewing environment.

It is the intensity of demands which is growing, so that their variety is being continuously multiplied. A single river is expected to bear having its meandering halted for flood control, its water withdrawn for industrial consumption, its current slowed for navigation, its rate stagnated with dams for hydroelectricity, its volume weighted with wastes, its bottom silted with sediment, and—all the while these events are happening—its value for fishing, recreation, and the aesthetics of housing developers maintained. It ought to be needless to say no one river can do all these things, no matter how rigidly classified different stretches of it might be for differing uses.

Yet it is not needless, because such multiple functions are exactly what the majority expect rivers to perform, either naturally or through the application of tax dollars under some program called one of "control." At the present time, the serving of so many demands by every river is impossible and of the same order as the human expectation that the weather will behave like the confetti swirling in a glass paperweight to imitate a blizzard. Sadly, it is the fate of such an expectation to be constantly disappointed, regardless of investments.

Still, this approach cannot be cast aside without careful consideration. Man has wrenched from nature multiple responses to meet his demands, not sparing his own health. While foods free of any artificial chemical from fertilizers, energizers, biocides, or growth regulators may be more healthful, the existence of these aids has been the solution for Thomas Malthus' prediction that food production could increase only arithmetically. In a crowded world of accelerating human demand, chemicals will continue to be used in agriculture for a wide variety of purposes. It may be possible to alternate or substitute what have been called biological and cultural controls for the purely chemical, yet even in these instances, chemicals will often be used as part of the process of reducing some natural force to compatibility with a limited human purpose.

The most severe charge to be brought against chemical control is not its intervention in natural processes. No control—chemical, biological, or cultural—will fail to do as much. The gravest charge is that the larger part of the menace from chemicals, such as those used in agriculture, is unexpected, irrelevant to the original purpose, and of no aid to any economic interest. The same results could happen to the biological controls, for they are in no way inherently benign or universally predictable. Some of those who work on genetic change to produce sterility in humanly unwanted species should consider the importance of that species as a food source to others and the extent to which such sterility might be "catching" to related but more economically valuable species. To concentrate on chemical control as a unique culprit is to miss the crux of the problem concerning man's relationship to nature.

To cite literature, for example, Dr. Jekyll sought chemical control, Baron Frankenstein biologic mastery, Dr. Miracle psychic sovereignty, and Faust jurisdiction over land, water, and man in the vast drainage scheme with which he closes his labors. None, it must be recalled, represents a particularly happy result so far as the subjects of the experiments are concerned, regardless of the approach used; and the same is true in the zone of real contacts between man and his environment.

the absence of historical inevitability in environmental control

It would be pleasant to say that because environmental control would be profitable or even necessary that it must come about. History, however, gives no such comfort. It offers little evidence of inevitability.

A recent history of the ecology of the Arno valley above Florence shows that it was deforested, under cultivation, and eroding by the first century A.D. This was intensified after the collapse of the western Roman empire by the arrival of malaria, which drove the settlers to the higher and more easily destroyed hills. In the seventh century A.D. the establishment of church and noble estates began the next thousand years of racking land, with the result that grave floods became common on the Florentine plain. This produced the first massive flood in 1117, with a subsequent record of one such every century. Following the great flood of 1333, Gianbattista Vico del Cilento called for reforestation of the hills to hold back the water and stop the river's silting. Failing that, Leonardo da Vinci called for dredging the Arno to prevent its building up above the plain. Neither of these courses was followed, then or later; and right through the massive flood of November, 1966, the same policy of unremitting exploitation was pursued. Nor has anything been done since. In the Arno, as in so many other valleys, it has stayed entirely in the abstract; and the only concrete aspect has been the steadiness in deterioration in the situation.

Neither general advantage, nor what has appeared as necessity since the fourteenth century, has been sufficient to dislodge the Arno's old patterns or those who profit from them. The profits shrink; the social costs become exorbitant which allow them to the few. The one constant has been salvation's refusal to come of its own accord. It has not done so in the Arno, and it will not do so anywhere else either.

Experience is both a hard and costly school, and, sadly, there are too many who cannot learn under that instruction either. Suffering can be a spur, but it can also be an inducement to a stupid fatalism; and that has been by far the commoner reaction. Very few have had the courage to toss aside fatalism and tackle the solutions having hope of success.

Within the next century, which is about the limit of the present generation's foreseeable future, there will be a steady escalation in the demands urban-industrial society will be making on its environment. Technology conquers nature whenever there is conflict between them. But up till now, too much of this conquest has produced what Ian McHarg calls the desolation of nature. Since man himself is not a technological artifact, this destruction becomes less and less tolerable as it comes closer to being total; and there seems little prospect of urban-industrial society's limiting its demands except as the result of some catastrophic break. What must be done, if the apprehended danger from the environmental perils is to be corrected, will be an ever-greater assumption of control over nature; and this must require a determination of what kind of nature man wants for himself.

At a time, for example, when air pollution may be costing residents of major American cities each year up to $1000 apiece, a survey in St. Louis showed residents there were not willing to spend in tax money over $1.00 per person per year to control it. They, of course, will spend far more, though not all as tax, if other areas follow California's plan to stop air pollution, including auto exhaust wastes, by the 1980s. Such an effort cannot be carried through for trifling outlays, for what will be happening is the revelation of the presently concealed costs to the ecology and society so that they will be fully a part of the accounting for the urban-industrial economy. Concededly such costs are not low now that they lie concealed, and they will not be shrunk by the act of bringing them into the open. Initially, in fact, the public may be both startled at their size and dismayed at the extent of the control needed to redress the balances.

man's duty to assume responsibility for nature

Gradually, yet steadily, man's urban-industrial society is moving toward a relationship with nature in which human investment and activity will be responsible for the bulk, if not the entirety, of processes within the ecumene previously left to natural functions composing the structure for man's environment. Already efforts are under way to break up the formation of hurricanes so as to protect easily ravaged coastal plains. In desert valleys through which seasonal winds blow, shifting the sand to the harm of new towns, it is suggested that walls be built like baffles in the mountain passes to shut out the disturbing winds from the valleys. With the removal of swamps, estuarine marshes, and ground water in zones adjoining the ocean, artificial structures must be constructed or sealers pumped below the surface in order to keep out the intrusion of salt water. One by one, as areas unfriendly to settlement are settled or as natural protectors are eliminated by economically competitive activity, there have to be these efforts and they have to produce successful results, if serious economic, social, or even cultural dislocations are not to follow.

Unfortunately, insofar as optimism over the assumption of this responsibility is concerned, the basis in knowledge for action of this sort is pitifully lacking. This is contrary to the assumption most often made: namely, that although man may be ignorant in the "soft" sciences concerning himself, such as psychology or economics, information in the "hard" sciences of biophysics is very quickly obtained. For the environment the exact opposite is true. Recent concern for the environment has compelled public administrators in the instances of new highway, harbor, or sewer projects to include ecologic sections in their protocols. It produces more than was known before; but in practical effect it is obeisance to a public image, for complex natural processes are not to be incidentally revealed.

Insofar as examination of the environment has been going on, it has been done by local units of government, by branches of state and federal administrations, or by universities and business enterprises. Not only has this been uncoordinated or even unaccounted for centrally, but the information has often been gathered in such a way that it cannot be coordinated because different techniques of measurement have been used. Weather records in the United States go back, in places, to the Revolution; but they are no help in determining the question of warming urban air masses since, over the decades, the temperature stations have been moved repeatedly further out from the city centers, often without noting it in the records. Using only this one example, it can be seen that the useful acquisition of knowledge for general purposes is a far different matter than picking up discrete fragments to meet the immediate needs of a nar-

rowly purposed project. Facts may be necessities, but if
not collected on a broadly conceived scale, they become
items for dead storage in warehouses.

What is needed in the contemporary urban-industrial
civilization is a monitoring system to indicate what is
happening in nature from the operation of such a civilization. Insofar as is now possible, base lines should be discovered, revealing the natural dynamics in particular situations so that forces present can be calculated to
determine whether they be for or against some local
human activity. Hopefully, this monitoring could lead to
determining the indexes of natural conditions, so that
both long-term warnings and quick emergency reactions
would result. The research of other agencies would either be coordinated or duplicated so that their results
could be integrated into a larger reporting process; the
monitoring agency itself would be backed up by a laboratory of broad ecologic curiosity.

From all this would emerge the hard data enabling
government effectively to reverse the trend. After all,
however purely biophysical the research may be (ab-
stracted from social considerations), nearly all of it must
involve today's politicoeconomic systems and must lead
to institutional changes. Such work will be highly contro-
versial, because it will lead to change, and change will
require large outlays and will interrupt existing, and
sometimes widespread, benefits for certain groups. If left
unsupported by nongovernmental pressure, both monitoring and laboratory work will find a safe routine within the
civil service—another kind of defeat. Indeed, this would
be worse, because the scene would be cluttered with the
lie that something significant had already been done and
had failed.

*the continuing
availability of choices*

The situation is too redeemable to allow a sense of
hopelessness or of a play-now-we-die-tomorrow excuse.
The legal and institutional means of effecting change are
appearing; and, in the absence of Alexander the Great to
drive through in a decade the changes for a thousand

years, they come slowly. A long-needed office of environmental quality has been established in the office of the President for the United States to have an effective national ecologic policy. Peers cannot regulate peers among administrators, and a cabinet-level department or an independent administrative agency could not do the job. The idea is scarcely a new one since Jeremy Bentham suggested the need for putting such a service in the executive office in the 1820s; and now, 150 years later, an office for regulating the quality of the environment, with powers like those of the Bureau of the Budget, is needed at the Presidential level. Legal and institutional changes take time and cannot be carried out overnight; but this environment control proposal is overdue. However slow the law may be, at *some* point in time action must be taken or natural events will take the initiative out of human hands.

Yet changing constitutions is time-consuming under conditions of conflict in a society where many groups participate in decisions and on a topic requiring considerable agreement if any change is to be operationally effective. Perhaps the present generation has renounced the right to ask, "What did posterity ever do for me?" Perhaps polls rightly show that 80 to 95 percent of the public is "concerned" with the ecology. Perhaps it is true the rich were "radicalized" by the Santa Barbara oil slick. All of these are doubtful propositions; but should they be true on any except the superficial level, it will still take time to make the needed changes.

Adequate time may not be available. Some think the ocean might cease to function by 1979 as a life-bearing entity because of the various pollutants entering it. Should this prove true, the prophecy could prove as useful to us as the handwriting on the wall was to Belshazzar. The time scales on both predictions leave a trifling scope for countermeasures. International conferences have been set up to study marine and natural resources; proposals are afoot to change a great laboratory on nuclear research, like Argonne, into one on the environment; and other, similar measures are in a concurrent beginning stage. But if 1979 is the deadline, institutionally hope is scant for first, redemption, and later, salvation. Nor, if the prediction is right, would failure to react much matter. Still, should such pessimism be wrong, so that the day of catastrophic break between man and nature proves sufficiently remote for counteraction to prevent it, then any opinion producing a sense of hopelessness now is very chancy business.

After all, man from his beginnings has been trying to isolate himself from natural food chains; and what currently is needed is either a limitation upon the perfection of the logical outcome or an artificial substitution for the knocked-out elements in the system. To produce the institutions capable of making *any* impact on such an ancient, almost atavistic tradition cannot be easy, or quick, or cheap, or painless. What must be insisted on now is hope for the needed changes in time to save man and nature from catastrophe and emphases on the means for carrying out those changes. It is the only way urban-industrial civilization can avoid arriving at its own self-appointed end. There is enough plausibility in catastrophe to justify a prompt undertaking of all the undramatic, petty-appearing changes needed to reverse the present accelerating trend. Fear can numb as well as spur; and there is no place for any more numbness in man's relationship to his environment. There must be, instead, the acutest sensitivity; and nothing must be allowed to dull its edges without full realization of the risks this entails.

Yet giving the conservative estimate its due and casting the appropriate aspersions on the radically pessimistic, the risk stands of irreversible damage from current industrial practices to every life form. How it comes will not be important if the ultimate result is loss of this planet's life within one to three generations. None of the costs of averting such a dire chance can outweigh in any terms the risk of its occurrence.

Man seems to be skittering around the edges of disaster in problems of food supply, the rates of land space to population, the effects of human numbers on his own psyche, the temperature of the atmosphere, the pollution of air and water, and the relationships concerning living organisms. To fail to handle any of these adequately could mean an abrupt end to the debate about the problem of man's relationship with nature—or, at most, would serve to move it over to an entirely metaphysical realm. For this reason those who take the gravest and most urgent view should set the pace, for there can be no tolerance for life should they prove to be the true Jeremiahs. Even if the pace they set is a fast one, it should be attempted. To do otherwise is to gamble with extinction.

the risks in the
processes of reversal

Even the means of preservation can themselves prove risky to human survival. In recent years great concern has been expressed over auto exhaust fumes. Beginning in California in 1966 and from there spreading to the rest of the United States, legislation has been passed to cut down on certain of these wastes through engine requirements. Even manufacturers in Europe and Asia have had to alter their cars' exhaust systems because of something that began on the statute books of a single American state.

The dangers to be eliminated include carbon monoxide and unconsumed hydrocarbons, which under sunny conditions are converted to various peroxides. Such wastes are creators of smog and probable contributors to environmentally related blood, respiratory, and eye diseases, among others. The means of eliminating them is to increase the efficiency of the operation of internal combustion engines. This means drawing large quantities of oxygen through the engine and producing nitrogen dioxide in sharply increasing amounts, even as the other exhaust output is being scaled down.

Unfortunately, evidence is very strong that this compound and certain other oxides of nitrogen resulting from the new control processes are mutagenic; and, in an area's atmosphere, they appear to be excellent as predictors for a full spectrum of cancers and other diseases such as emphysema and asthma. Only the presence of sulphur dioxide and, for more limited purposes, nickel in the air have been said to be equally good predictors. Assuming this proves to be more than a statistical phenomenon on further genetic investigation, the preservation techniques themselves will prove to have been exacerbators or, at least, a matter of having exchanged one set of pollutants dangerous to health for others of similar peril. The mere fact that smog may be reduced would prove in such a case to be a more apparent than real solution, which might act more to mask the crisis than clear it up.

The point of this illustration is *not* to express opposition to auto exhaust controls. The amount of waste put into the atmosphere by these engines must be cut sharply for reasons other than those tied directly to human health. Increasing smog is producing severe traffic tie-ups at major air terminals and is contributing to rising air turbidity levels, which may be having considerable effects on both this planet's reception of solar energy and the ability of plants to photosynthesize oxygen. In fact, until recent statistical studies it seemed as if increasing air pollution was a cause without a disease, and only the "hunches" of some doctors kept insisting that there were connections. It is only very recently that evidence is beginning to come in showing rises in deaths from emphysema and related lung diseases that, like the general incidence of cancer, are well predicted by the escalating levels of certain chemicals and minerals in the air.

It may be, of course, that these are the vulnerable segments of the population, the ones who would have died in the old days from the now diminished scourges of tuberculosis, pneumonia, and infectious fevers. This is an estimate very hard to prove one way or another. In any case it is not a sufficient reason for indifference to acquiring further knowledge; the example of auto exhaust control shows how small has been past knowledge and how misleading the apparently certain facts. What is revealed once again as being badly needed is further investigation and the permanent institutions to sponsor research on the environment into the indefinite future.

When even the solutions to recognized problems turn out either to reveal difficulties standing in face of the known ones or, worse, to create themselves more severe situations, the needs for such continuing research are clear. Otherwise, to speak ironically, Americans may make the supreme sacrifice of giving up cigarettes only to see the rates of emphysema and lung cancer continuing to rise. Knowledge is a tricky business and its pursuit is not to be smugly terminated. It is possible that in some of the particulate matter from air pollution which needs cleaning up are trace minerals that serve as health protectors as well as those that imperil persons absorbing them. Copper, which in large amounts is quite harmful, shows as a negative predictor of a wide variety of diseases and its presence in trace quantities may counteract the hurtful effects of others in a way that makes gross pollution conditions bearable. It may be only a possibility, but it indicates that correction of the effects of urban-industrial systems is not likely to be easy.

In the case of aerial waste, as in most other cases, the concentrated concern, when it has appeared, has been with the direct effect on individual life or organ systems. Where such systems have shown no higher death rates or gross malformation, there has seemed to be little reason to show interest, for the assumption made is that no harm has occurred. Yet this assumption may be wrong and hence extremely risky. What may be occurring to the apparently unaffected organisms is a low rate of mutagenesis which, particularly in the relatively more complex and longer-lived species, may be very slow in detection but, when detected, will turn out to be as grave as the more immediately dramatic results in systems suffering from direct reactions.

When death rates from a particular disease merely show a steady increase, it becomes much harder for the public to treat this as anything other than a function of nature. Should the totals finally ascend to a high percentage of the bills of mortality and should the total death rate rise, the slowness of such developments may cause the public to see a perilous outcome as merely another part of reality. So also it is with mutagenesis, which is the greatest risk from new treatments for alleviating human and environmental sicknesses.

Abrupt effects of a mutagen are relatively rare. Far more likely is a mutagen that, by accelerating senescence, would increase the rates of death from tumorous, cardiovascular, renal, and respiratory diseases. Some see a connection between the increase of these diseases and the rise in the atmosphere of sulphur dioxide, nitrogen dioxide, and trace metals such as vanadium, cadmium, nickel, and other substances not previously present in the atmosphere or in food sources in the current quantities. Yet this is very difficult to prove, even though, should the hypothesis prove true, medical research on the subject would ultimately be little more than historical. It is not hard to assume that proof might come too late for an irreversible condition, but when the mutagenesis may be spread over many generations, it is not easy to stir up much interest. Situations remote in time, even if certain, arouse small present concern, however horrible, and this indifference is accentuated when the distant crisis is just a possibility. The future thereby becomes another country whose citizens are no responsibility for this generation.

the requirement to choose man's future

What remains essential for any generation is summed up by the question that ecologist Kenneth E. F. Watt believes the leaders of each generation should ask themselves: How long does mankind plan for survival on this or any other planet? Ten years? Ten generations? Forever? The answer determines the existence and the significance of humanity.

There is, after all, no guarantee that what appear as remote crises will prove to keep such comfortable distances. Paul Ehrlich, Lamont Cole, and other ecologists, who see an interlocking series of crises in the environment stemming from direct effects as being scarcely more than a decade away, may be right. But even if they are wrong and the time of the emergency will not come until later, the questions still remain: How long does man plan to be around? Is it forever, or should we start discounting for a shorter span?

Assuredly, the shorter the predetermined span, the less investment need be made in environmental maintenance. In that event, effort should be concentrated on the making, as an artifact, of disposable history. But if that is the decision, there ought to be no repinings when the last moments of the discount process are at hand, even by people not yet born who never had a part in the choice. The present generation must determine whether a short human existence is most desirable; whether human effects on the environment can be controlled; what must be the institutions needed for carrying out such work; the processes for internalizing the work's costs in the production mechanism; and what role man plans for himself during his time in nature. These are basic queries, and the means for obtaining their answers must be initiated.

Predictions about the future are a common commodity. The National Agricultural Chemicals Association's 1969 convention was assured that the American farm output could expect to increase fivefold through heavy reliance on the products of the association's members. If this prophecy is an accurate one, it will correlate with rapidly rising demands on land space in the countries advanced in the processes of urban-industrial civilization. The most vulnerable competitor in this conflict is recreation, but agriculture is not much more secure. In California and Florida only a noneconomic man would keep an acre in citrus at an income of $4,000 per acre when he can put it in a subdivision at up to $30,000 for the same acre—and less profitable crops than citrus only hone the argument. Just as agriculture developed in valleys where the forests were thickest, displacing the wild trees with cultivated crops, so are the cities of the plain ousting farms, forests, and parks alike.

A modern city, with its nimbus of "slurb," casts such a spell as far as 75 miles from itself; and many factors enter into this effect. The rising assessments and tax rates are one, so that local public policy in areas proximate to large cities acts as a prod to conversion for urban purposes. Interest rates and inflation are another, as witnessed by the spread of mobile homes, each with its plot and septic tank in the exurban zones. More ground goes continuously to urban use, without regard for the limited amount of land available for the total of human purposes. As Lord Molson has said, there is no such thing as truly vacant or derelict land and in the long run it is economic as well as aesthetic to preserve the options of alternative uses.

Once land has been taken from forest, parks, farm, wet land, beach, or other use for city expansion, it is nearly impossible to reclaim it from the urban expanse. Given the increasing trend to city living, the expansion of urban-industrial civilization with its rise in demands and expectations, the growth in population, and in the more affluent countries, the urge toward recreation away from the city, it is not hard to see a crisis in the making. Ignoring it and hoping it will depart of its own accord scarcely seems the better course.

The truth is so modest that it seems trite to point it out, but one can only agree with the insistences of a group of conservation lawyers at the September, 1969, Airlie House conference. They demanded that the burden of proof of harm be shifted from those who want to preserve a present use to those wanting a larger economic return on their cash investments; that initiative come more often before the damage rather than after the fact; that government live up to the formal orders to take ecology into account; that legal rules be developed both to cut the cost and expedite the rise of judicial and administrative processes for environmental preservation; that land and other resources be regarded as a trust to be guarded against transitory and arbitrary abuses; and that the Ninth Amendment in the Bill of Rights guarantee the people against encroachments on the resources necessary to their existence. Whether there is absolute agreement with the reasoning of the lawyers, their call for action is a modest one in social terms and in relation to the doom inherent in the crisis between man's urban-industrial civilization and its environment.

There is, certainly, an awareness of doom as a possibility through much of the world. Especially in the industrially advanced states where capital has greater availability for nonincome-producing uses, corrective measures are being taken. Usually, however, they are in terms of what the productive process can afford in relation to the market rather than what the environment must have to become or remain viable. It is for this reason that ecologists continue to be critical even when air quality standards are met or water quality is found to have been improved. While any raising of the quality of the environment is good in itself, the general condition of the human ecumene remains the issue of greatest importance; and for it there has been no across-the-board remission. An economy willing to pay almost as much per pound for the disposal of solid waste as it does for raw sugar has simply not yet arrived at the proper allocation of values. Under such conditions the brightest hope is that the task may be made easier as a result of the high price attached to the failure to internalize costs.

Not even in cash terms is the present approach cheap, and as for the larger world beyond man's interests, the present human conduct has within it all the expenses of an ultimate bankruptcy. The skill to solve the problems man has with nature are available; and through those skills, whatever the knowledge now lacking, the needed information could be obtained. The technical problems of the twentieth century have more often proved to be solvable than insoluble, and the technical side of man's difficulties with his environment would be no exception.

Far more problematic is whether the interior processes of humanity summarized under such topics as politics, economics, and psychology are prepared to initiate the necessary changes. If the will exists to choose another way of coping with nature, the technical and institutional alterations needed can be carried through. But if the basic will behind such an option is lacking, then technical and institutional improvements become palliatives that can slow but not prevent the impending severe environmental crisis. If man decides to refuse to change traditional human behavior relative to nature, then he can only hope the doomsayer to have been wrong and that life will win this very dangerous kind of roulette. The evidence, however, grows constantly stronger that the game played this way is for losers only.

REFERENCES

Man in the City of the Future, Richard Eels and Clarence Walton, eds., New York: Arkville Press, 1968.

Georg Borgstrom, *Too Many: A Study of Earth's Biological Limitations,* New York: Macmillan, 1969.

Harrison Brown, James Bonner, and John Weir, with a preface by Lee Dubridge, *The Next Hundred Years: Man's Natural and Technological Resources,* New York: Viking Press, 1963.

Paul P. Harbrecht, *Toward the Paraproprietal Society: An Essay on the Nature of Property in 20th Century America,* New York: Twentieth Century Fund, 1960.

James Willard Hurst, *Law and Conditions of Freedom in the 19th Century United States,* Madison: University of Wisconsin Press, 1956.

Edward Hyams, *Soil and Civilization,* London: Thames and Hudson, 1952.

Herman Kahn, Anthony J. Wiener, and others, *The Year 2000,* New York: Macmillan, 1967.

Earl Finbar Murphy, *Governing Nature,* Chicago: Quadrangle Books, 1967.

Lynn White, Jr., *Machina ex Deo: Essays in the Dynamism of Western Culture,* Cambridge: MIT, 1968.

index

167

index

Solid waste, disposal of, 63–65, 66–67, 69, 82, 157
Southwest, American, 50, 78, 79
Spanish tree-planting requirement, 30
Species, importance to man of any, 58, 59, 68, 119
Specificity, cost, 81, 82, 83, 95, 99, 101, 105, 118, 155, 157
State environmental agencies, formation of, 28, 92, 103, 137, 147
State park, first state-created, in United States, 31
Static, natural definition of, 6, 7, 9–10, 17, 37, 44, 45, 51, 116, 134
Stewart, Dugald, and forests, 29
Stock resources, 11, 68, 135, 136
Streams, effect of wasteful lumbering on, 22, 65; gross nineteenth-century effluent in, 23, 47, 65; reasons for early silting of, 23, 24, 46–47, 65, 112
Strip-mining, effects of, 64; restoration from, 65
Sturgeon fishing, decline of, 47
Subsidy, cities receiving softwood, 20, 21
Subsistence and environment, 36, 37, 49, 90–91
Suffocation, threat from waste, early problem, 23
Swamp Lands Act, 75
Swamps, fiscal returns from draining, 5, 7; functions of, 4, 7–8, 9, 146–147; how man creates, 7–8; importance of biota in, 135; natural reasons for, 8; traditional views concerning, 3–4; varied cultural responses to, 5, 6, 7

Swiss Family Robinson, 55–56
Synergizing, problems in food, 90–91, 126

Technology and environmental control, 17, 20, 35, 40, 43, 47, 49, 54, 55, 60, 82, 101, 102, 108, 116, 119, 125, 130, 134, 135, 136, 138, 145, 148, 154, 157
Thames, condition of, 24
Timber Culture Act, 31
Timber thieves, 87–88, 89
Time spans in natural replacement, 10–11, 45, 46, 50, 70, 107, 129, 138, 149, 154

UNESCO, 13, 105
United Nations, 1972 conference on environment, 105, 149; and resources, 73
United States, use of resources for labor and capital in, 21, 75, 78, 100, 112, 118, 139–140
United States Marine Resources Council, 107
Unity of man and nature, current impossibility of, 12, 45, 56, 134
Urban-commercial civilization, 38
Urban growth, anticipated, 134, 140, 150, 155–156; risks of, 155–156
Urban-industrial civilization, 40, 57, 58, 61, 64, 69, 70, 71–72, 73, 78, 90, 91, 100, 102, 104, 107–108, 121, 126, 133, 134, 136, 141, 142, 145, 146, 148, 153, 155, 156, 157

Value, expressed in calories, 115, 116; expressed in ergs, 115, 116; problem of expressing, in cash terms, 110, 112, 113, 115, 116, 118, 124, 130, 135, 140